M000205054

To. Kendra —

POPCORN POPPIN' ON THE APRICOT TREE

With blessings
& joy this

holiday season . . .

Wum Regards —

Faith Paulus   11/25/04

POPCORN POPPIN' ON THE APRICOT TREE

written by

FAITH PAULUS

TATE PUBLISHING & *Enterprises*

Tate Publishing
& Enterprises

Popcorn Poppin on the Apricot Tree
by Faith Paulus
Copyright © 2006 by Faith Paulus. All rights reserved.
Visit www.tatepublishing.com for more information.

No part of this publication may be reproduced, stored in a retrieval system or transmitted in any way by any means, electronic, mechanical, photocopy, recording or otherwise without the prior permission of the author except as provided by USA copyright law.
Scripture quotations marked "NLT" are taken from the *Holy Bible, New Living Translation*, Copyright © 1996. Used by permission of Tyndale House Publishers, Inc. All rights reserved.
The opinions expressed by the author are not necessarily those of Tate Publishing, LLC.
This book is designed to provide accurate and authoritative information with regard to the subject matter covered. This information is given with the understanding that neither the author nor Tate Publishing, LLC is engaged in rendering legal, professional advice. Since the details of your situation are fact dependent, you should additionally seek the services of a competent professional.

Book design copyright © 2006 by Tate Publishing, LLC. All rights reserved.
Cover design by Melanie Harr-Hughes
Interior design by Taylor Rauschkolb

Published in the United States of America

ISBN: 1–5988646–1-0

06.10.26

This book is dedicated to Carolyn Navarre Peters, who for more than forty years has been a source of comfort to fellow patients and staff members alike. May her angelic presence stay alive and well in the halls of our state mental institutions, long after her departure into a better world.

Acknowledgments

A drienne de Noyelles has proven to be not only a superb editor, but also a constant friend who has challenged me to stretch my writing skills while encouraging me to explore the untapped emotional arenas of my imagination. In *Popcorn Poppin' on the Apricot Tree,* Adrienne welcomes my innovative grammatical approach with her own brand of polish, as together we defy typical editorial standards in favor of the unbiased perception of a child's mind. In addition, the passion and playfulness that she brings to the table has made Adrienne de Noyelles a joy to work with in this "divinely appointed" team effort.

Special gratitude to each of my siblings, Lisa, Jean, Joe, and Theresa: The years together have been filled with fun, humor, and adventure, as we share a stimulating solidarity and zest for life that simply cannot be replaced with anyone but each other. I am supremely blessed for the camaraderie of this creative family as we persist in cheering each other on to unlimited personal and spiritual growth.

And where would we be without the support and inspiration of a True Best Friend? I am honored to share this distinction with my own, Kathy Finley. Together we have forged through our tentative twenties, tumultuous thirties, and the surprisingly fabulous forties, armed with gazillions of Self Help Books, twenty-plus years of *"Oprah,"* and hours upon hours of stimulating conversation.

I would also like to express my appreciation for the many other enlightening friendships that have graced my life's path with insight and humor, including: Mona Ciampa, Gina Cinque, Libby Hinson, Tony Anthony, Denise Denton, Susanne Swenddal, Gloria Eck, Patty Francis, Lynn Jackson, Nancy Day, Terri Patillo, and Michael Sosebee. True friendships serve as the colorful threads that weave the fabric of a writer's imagination, and I am eternally grateful to those mentioned, as well as those who are not.

A very special thank-you to my husband, Bo Paulus, who too often was left waiting for me as I arrived late at the restaurant, breathless with "being in the moment with my book." Always forgiving, accepting, and encouraging, you saw me through each stage of my writings as patiently as you have seen me through each stage of our enchanting relationship. Now, as we venture into the first year of our wonderful marriage, I revel in the fact that you, Bo, are truly the Embracer Of My Dreams.

Finally, I would like to thank God for his innate ability to place us all in the exact environment that is necessary for our growth and happiness, and for allowing me the honor of being an inspiring channel for His good.

You saw me before I was born.
Every day of my life was recorded in your book
Every moment was laid out
Before a single day had passed

Psalm 139: 16 (NLT)

Edith Navarre,
High School Graduation
circa early 1900s

Bill Peters, High School Graduation - 1941

Carolyn Navarre, High School Graduation - 1942

Faith Ann Peters, High School Graduation - 1975

September 1964

The hands of the large black clock ticked menacingly slow as I doodled at my desk, trying to ignore the background drone of Sister Marie Josetta. There seemed to be no actual evidence of feet as she floated among the colorful reading chairs—though sometimes I was treated to a black-tipped toe shyly peeking out from underneath the hem of her gown. Secretly, I yearned to have the strict nun trip over the chairs just once, her habit skirts flying up to reveal the all-mysterious Nun Panties. But my Sinful Thoughts were thwarted as Sister Josetta skillfully wove her way around each small chair using only the Eyes In The Back Of Her Head.

There could be no doubt about it: The Order of the Sisters of St. Joseph were in command at St. Mary's Elementary School in Lansing, Michigan. Our school was part of a Gothic cathedral dating back more than one hundred years, its sanctuary filled with the smoky aroma of incense and the salty smells of the cracked leather pews. Heavy, red velvet drapes roped off the imposing altar, where glistening gold goblets reigned with silver candlesticks on tablecloths of the purest white linen. The scars of time had left interesting facial shapes on the rough-hewn rocks that huddled behind the altar with smug authority. One of them bore an uncanny resemblance to Father Fedewa, who seemed unaware of this chiseled twin hovering over his shoulder as if to correct the elderly priest's pronunciation of the Latin phrases. Of course, any error on Father Fedewa's part would have been easily overlooked, since the real meaning of *this* foreign language was a Mystery Unto Itself.

All too often, the congregation had to take cover from several bats that swooped down from the swirling mist of the belfry. This eerie performance could always be counted on to terrify the younger children, who were well versed in the tale of The First Grade Student Who Had a Bat Get Tangled in Her Hair. It was said that The Bat was still embedded in the once-beautiful platinum locks of this unfortunate child, where it would forever nest with its young.

Occasionally, threads of golden sunlight would stream through the cracks of the stained-glass windows, dancing across the pews like iridescent fairies. Their whispered promises of flight seemed the only relief to the cave-like existence within this fortress of gloom.

Connected to the cathedral by a musty corridor was its Gothic equivalent: St. Mary's Elementary. Here, the nuns could be found pacing through dark, narrow hallways, casting long shadows as they went about their early-morning prayer. Accompanied by the clicking of rosaries and the fresh smell of starch, the nuns quietly inspected our wrinkled uniforms with a sigh of deliverance from our imperfect souls.

The taunting hands of the Big Black Clock were continuing their merciless crawl as Sister Josetta, with a heroic effort to "let some air into this muggy room," successfully pried open the heavy wooden window. The heavenly vapor of freshly raked foliage and distant burning leaves lingered briefly, before whisking hurriedly from the stifling classroom—as if to torture my imprisoned spirit with its tantalizing aroma. I was beginning to suspect that the up-coming Reading Hour might be the only shred of stimulation to another dreary afternoon at St. Mary's Elementary.

My mother, a College Professor, had taught me to read before I reached Kindergarten. Nevertheless, in an unusual stretch of hu-mility, I had been keeping my dormant talents Under Wraps—until yesterday. It was right after lunch, when all of the second graders were being sorted into biased little groups of Reading Levels that I had decided to reveal my true intelligence. Standing tall beside my desk, and after just the right pause, I had blown right through Dick and Jane—successfully stunning my entire audience. Later, it was determined that I had broken all the records by reading at a stag-gering speed of "Eighth Grade Level." Since I had been struggling all year with my Basic Math problems, this little preview of my real brilliance had resulted in a satisfying new wrinkle on the already furrowed brow of Sister Josetta. Clearly, the perplexed nun had pegged me as having a Learning Disability, and probably couldn't wait to ban me to the Little Red Trailers that were tucked discreetly outside St. Mary's school building. Even so, I was now enjoying my popular new Title as "Chairman" for the prestigious Snowflake Reading Group. My brother Joe, close enough in age to share the same grade, had not even been jealous that day, as he made way for me around the circle of miniature blue chairs.

I went on to study the bangs of Sister Josetta which protruded from her veil in a perfect little sausage curl, and decided this time, my sister was Telling The Truth. "All nuns are really bald," Jean had recently confided in a rare moment of generosity for her superior third grade knowledge. Then, lowering her voice to a discreet hush, she had also exposed the "well known fact" that "Nun Bangs could be purchased separately at the Woolworth's Five and Dime." We had even gone on to discuss their odd apparel: It seemed to me that God's imagination was much too colorful to have signed off on the simple black-and-white garments that the nuns sported with an air of fashionable authority. Besides, I had later told my sister, the gowns were clearly a knock-off of the highly original Penguin family. These were called Habits, not gowns, Jean had corrected me, because the nuns were forced to wear the same one every day.

As I returned to drawing the whiskers of a smiling cat, the mysterious box on the wall—which contained our principal's voice— suddenly came alive. "Annie Peters," the P.A. system crackled, "please come to the Sister Superior's office at once."

There had not been a classroom disturbance of this kind since November 22nd of last year, when on my birthday Sister Superior had made the unexpected announcement that we would be all be given a day off from school. At the time, I thought this could only mean that America would be *joining* me in my birthday celebration.

But later that afternoon, instead of the usual gala in which I would finally get to play The Starring Role, everyone remained glued to the Hi Fi television that my mother had just won as a Door Prize. Apparently, somebody named President Kennedy had been assassinated by a mysterious man who was still making his Big

Getaway. And even though Mr. Cronkite appeared every fifteen minutes with more Late Breaking News, there was not even one announcement to the people of America that Annie Peters had reached the age of six.

For days afterwards, I was plagued with the same black-and-white images of a casket draped with an American flag, which was it seemed, *never* going to make it into the ground. On top of that, someone who happened to be at the Scene Of The Crime, had caught the whole thing on a fuzzy Home Videotape, and we were all forced to watch the gruesome shooting over and over again—just so we would never forget. During this tragedy, tiny rivers of blood stained the very fashionable suit of our elegant First Lady, who reminded me of the lovely *Snow White*, as she remained poised and serene through it all. The most disturbing outcome of the whole ordeal however, was that after almost a whole year, I was still having trouble shaking a secret crush that I had somehow acquired for little John-John. I might even have considered marrying the captivating young fellow—if he were closer to my age.

"Annie . . . *please* come back to Earth!" I shielded my eyes from the harsh glare of the fluorescent light and found myself looking straight into the flared nostrils of Sister Josetta. One wayward hair curled defiantly from her thin upper lip, while sparks of icy-blue flashed from crinkled eyes. Clearly, this little interruption had not been part of the day's agenda.

Taking a quick mental inventory of any possible trouble I might have caused, I risked a quick sideward glance at my brother. But his half-hearted shrug made it clear that he couldn't be bothered with *my* problems. This time, I was On My Own.

Finally, I decided that even a lecture would beat this increasingly dreary scene. Mustering all the dignity of a Prisoner Of War humbly accepting his fate, I secretly reveled in the curious eyes that remained glued to me as I clattered noisily out of the classroom.

After all, it was my Classmate Duty to make the most of this un-expected interruption.

Sister Josetta's shrill reminder, "And Young Ladies know how to march *quietly!*" was cut off just as an extra nudge of my saddle oxford shoe caused the heavy classroom door to slam shut.

After doing a quick cartwheel in the middle of the empty hallway and taking a peek in the restroom mirror just for fun, I arrived at Sister Superior's office to find my mother perched anx-iously at the towering oak desk.

Because of her kindly voice and disposition, the Sister Superior was one of my favorite nuns at St. Mary's. Since our family was considered quite large, the nuns tended to greet each of us into the new school year with the predestined label of "One Of The Peters Children." Even though judging others was supposed to be a Venial Sin, it was clear that the behavior of the previous sibling could make or break your entire year. Sister Superior, however, seemed to regard each one of us as an individual instead of just another member of the clan.

Quickly clearing her desk, she made a place for me by pulling up an extra little chair. If it weren't for the troubled look in the nun's warm brown eyes, I would have thought we three ladies were simply getting together for a tea party.

My mother was wearing an elegant linen suit from her Glamour Days, which looked quite out of place in Sister Superior's barren office. One lone strand of brown hair spilled out from under the veil of an old ivory pillbox hat that Jean and I had often fought over during Dress Up Time. Her stiff posture reminded me for a moment of the lovely statue that hovered elegantly over the first floor landing. Saint Theresa wore a gown of delicate blue folds and an expression so pure, that I made it a daily habit to salute her with a quick Sign Of The Cross, just for gracing our school with her extraordinary beauty.

Just like Saint Theresa, my mother seemed aware of my presence, but did not reach out and give me the usual Bear Hug. Instead, long white gloves that were hiding her pretty, tapered fingertips tapped nervously on the scarred desk.

Sister Superior and I both listened very carefully as my mother tearfully related the reason for her Surprise Visit: There was to be a Kidnapping involving me and my other four siblings, and it was to take place that very afternoon on the playground of St. Mary's Elementary. The Kidnapper, it seemed, had a special interest in taking me; a flattering thought that seemed far more appealing than spending the next hour with *Dick and Jane*. I immediately tried to imagine what the captor looked like, but could only visualize my loving daddy whisking us away to a deserted island, just like Robinson Crusoe . . .

While I was mentally constructing the makeshift fort—complete with American flag—that my family would tirelessly build under a crystal-blue sky, my concentration was shattered by Sister Superior firmly calling me to attention. With quiet assurance, she explained to both of us that there had never been, and probably never would be, a Kidnapping at St. Mary's Elementary School.

My mother, remembering her usual impeccable manners, grew silent for a moment as she considered the principal's suggestion. I caught my breath with a glimmer of hope that in a last minute miracle, she was going to come to her senses after all. But after flashing a gracious smile of apology, my mother continued with even more vivid details of the upcoming abduction.

Sister Superior was just settling into the worn creases of her burgundy leather chair with an air of feigned interest in this lively story, when I suddenly recalled the Box with the Plain Brown Wrapper. . . .

Mr. Mailman had rung the doorbell with packages for both my mother and me that day. I was the proud new owner of an

Ant Farm that my father had ordered from the back of my favorite comic book. Just like the advertisement had warned, it had taken exactly six long weeks for my package to appear. This fact could be proven by the pencil marks that were carefully concealed under the lid of my school desk. I had also spent every afternoon, through both snow and shine, perched on our front-yard picket fence to find out if my Very Important Package had arrived. I knew this Act Of Grace would surely speed things along.

And then, just when I was beginning to wonder if I was *ever* going to have the opportunity to "Amaze All My Friends," as the advertisement promised, the Ant Farm finally arrived. Mr. Mailman seemed relieved as he gently laid the package in my arms, pointing out that it was specifically addressed to Ms. Annie Peters. This meant, Mr. Mailman patiently explained, that no one else in my family—including my brother, Joe—was allowed to open it. That was The Law.

My mother was not having as much fun with her new toy. After rushing The Mailman out the front door with a look of alarm, she had thrown the box out into the backyard and fled into the kitchen. Later, she took me aside and calmly explained that *her* Very Important Package contained a dangerous bomb. Worse, the package had been sent by a Very Bad Person who wanted to hurt our family.

When my father came home from work that day, much earlier than usual, he reminded my mother that the package only contained Christmas cookie cutters that she had recently ordered by mail. Though he laughed this off in his usual lighthearted way, we all had begun to notice the worry that seemed to deepen the lines in his forehead with each new Episode.

For a while now, my mother's bedtime had been scheduled even earlier than my own. We children had been warned not to disturb her, since She Was Not Feeling Well. Even more irritating were the private Slumber Parties that were being held in her honor on the Fifth Floor of St. Lawrence Hospital. I was beginning to suspect, with a twinge of envy, that her new early bedtime was probably due to a lack of sleep from all the fun.

In an effort to learn more about my increasingly mysterious household, I had begun taking late-night escapades downstairs with a perfect alibi—the mandatory glass of milk—should I be questioned by those who held a higher rank. This was also the ideal opportunity to slide down the long ivory banister in blissful solitude, free from the taunts of more adventurous siblings who were always too willing to push me from behind.

At the end of my late night flight, I could always count on finding my father resting in his Lay-Z-Boy, gazing thoughtfully out the window. If I timed my slide perfectly, I could make it from the end of the banister into his lap in one fell swoop, turning his worried expression into a tender smile as he made way for me to snuggle in closer.

With my fingertips, I loved to trace the faded picture of the mystical rose that was tautly displayed on the muscle of my father's strong left arm. According to my brother, the flower had suddenly appeared while my father was in the Navy, and in love with a woman who bore the same name. Even now, a majestic ribbon floated under the rose, which had once flaunted the name of the perpetual young nymph who would forever be attached to my father's past. Upon marrying my mother, it seemed there had been a feeble attempt to remove the time-weary rose, but the faded letters could still be observed in the light of a clear dawn perhaps as a subtle memory of a more liberating love . . .

Taking the opportunity for a little one-on-one chat, I would try to gather information from my father by twisting the corners of his mouth back up into the opposite position of a smile. "Daddy,"

I would tease, "when are you going to turn that frown upside down?"

Hoisting me up on his shoulder, my father would respond by running back up the staircase and tossing me into bed like a sack of potatoes. This little game could always be counted on to make me laugh out loud, while my father smothered his own amusement for the sake of sleeping children.

The sounds of his fading footsteps, mingled with the soothing tones of Johnny Carson, provided a certain sense of comfort; but they didn't quite make up for the special Goodnight Kisses that I had come to cherish from my mother—kisses that were getting harder and harder to come by.

Now, as my mother struggled to reorient herself in the Principal's Office, I presented my sweetest smile to welcome her back. Instead, her startled eyes darted over my shoulder, as if wistfully bidding farewell to The Demon that was furiously trying to make its escape. Feeling a pang of jealousy, I turned to confront The One who held my mother in his thrall—and was disappointed to find a space as empty as my mother's melancholy stare.

After one last feeble attempt to warn Sister Superior of the mysterious villain who was making his way to the playground at that very moment, my mother finally gave up. Hating to see her look so defeated, I gave my mother an extra hug. "Don't worry," I consoled her. "No one would ever be so lucky as to be kidnapped on a Monday."

My mother's eyes, which usually held all the quiet colors of a sea-green ocean, appeared to flicker around the room with unusual sparkles of light. And upon closer range, I could see that her makeup had been hurriedly applied (unlike the perfectly drawn lips and cheeks of Saint Theresa, which happened to be the exact shade of my favorite Carnation Pink crayon). No, I had been mistaken. There was no resemblance between my mother's frantic expression and the calm, clear gaze of Saint Theresa at all.

A few minutes later, I was heading toward the Snowflake reading chairs with a sinking feeling in my heart that went beyond the despair of facing a long afternoon. I was slowly losing my mother to the Other World, a place that my family could never be a part of. The whisperings of these People In The Other World were gradually winning the race to invade her mind. They were surely coming to get her, and it would be up to my mother to find her own way home.

2

November 1964

Nestled in The Attic amidst yellowed photographs and letters was a cardboard box teeming with tearstained and joyful journeys that were Before My Time. I pored over the details they contained with the determination of a scientist who is on the verge of an evolutionary discovery, having decided that in order to uncover the reasons for my mother's more frequent Episodes, I needed to piece together her past.

First, I rehashed what I already knew: my mother had the I.Q. of a genius, with an uncanny ability to absorb information at an astounding speed. (My father could always be counted on to volunteer this fact, still preening over such a remarkable woman falling prey to his average American mentality.)

Next, I carefully went through each of my mother's old yearbooks, carefully studying each page for hidden clues. It seemed that the sheltered, all-girls private school known as The Marywood Academy had seen Carolyn Marie Navarre blossom into an avid horsewoman, artist, and tennis player. Her beauty, charm, and grace did not go unnoticed by the admiring seniors in her graduating class, who graced her with the title "Most Likely To Succeed."

This impressive caption, emblazoned under the photograph of a beautiful young lady wearing a cashmere sweater and an air of quiet confidence, seemed a far cry from my mother's current situation. Why lately, she was not even participating in her usual exercises with Jack LaLanne on television. Instead, she was hunched over the ironing board with a mountain of school uniforms that patiently waited to be pressed for the next School Day. It seemed to me that spending three hours a day on this boring task was a pretty poor exchange for a glamorous, high-flying career. Even so, I agreed with my father that there must be a more interesting pastime than watching a timid man in black leotards encouraging the women of America to Get In Shape.

In between the scrawled autographs that consumed both covers of her college yearbook, there were brief passages of my mother's new campus life. "Every square inch of these grounds seem to swallow me up in seasonal beauty," she wrote. "I am completely entranced with this orderly world that exists for the sole purpose of stretching the intellect."

By the time she graduated from college—with Honors—my mother had found a new passion for creating extraordinary oil paintings, and was taking frequent trips to Europe with friends to pursue her artistic ambitions.

One of these paintings hung slightly askew above my mother's

Reading Chair in the living room downstairs as if trying to keep its balance. Within brightly colored dollops of oil, my mother had managed to capture the serene expression of a delicate ballerina in a pink tutu whirling at a captivating speed, her hair a swirling mass of uncaught tendrils. Lost in her own thoughts, the lovely ballerina seemed blissfully unaware of the strokes of gray and black gathering quietly like rain clouds all around her . . .

Abby, a petite, brown-haired woman, had skin that looked just like my grandmother's finest bone china. She also held the honorable title of being my mother's One And Only Best Friend. Whenever she came over to Pitch In—usually with her own four children in tow—child-rearing suddenly took on as much excitement as the teen-age adventures that were still the topic of much discussion between Abby and my mother. I loved to watch my mother's expression become softer whenever Abby was around.

David, Abby's son, was the same age as my sister Jean. Because his dark good looks and her unusual beauty made a nice combination, Jean and her Best Friend, Cathy McNamara, agreed that David and Jean would be married one day. It was expected, they told me, since Arranged Marriages were the custom with families who had been friends for years.

I often wondered why David seemed to know nothing of this traditional ceremony that was destined to take place. I also secretly feared that someone would arrange to put me with Fat Tommy, since his parents were quite chummy with mine—and we had the unfortunate circumstance of being the same age.

It was no secret in our family that anything involving money was guaranteed to get Joe's attention. Therefore, one recent rainy day, after running out of playtime ideas, I decided to Make A Bet with my brother, who was intent on ignoring me behind his latest Spiderman comic book. Boldly stepping up to the staircase, I announced that I could easily insert my knee between the wood spindles of the staircase banister without getting stuck. To my complete horror, my knee really did get jammed as two of the white posts, in an effort to Teach Me A Lesson, gripped my knee with a supernatural strength. Laughing at my plight, Joe absolutely refused to get help until I started crying real tears.

My mother made the bad decision to call an ambulance and then quickly took to her bed, as if the whole ordeal were Too Much To Bear. As if the day's events were not already degrading enough, the Fireman had to saw through the banister while all the neighborhood children stood peering into the open door from our front yard. Watching the teeth of the large saw grind dangerously near my leg, I began to send up long, soulful wails. After all, I wasn't interested in becoming an amputee like Sammy, the Korean War Veteran who lived next door. Wearing a scarf of the American Flag on his head as if it made up for the loss of a leg, Sammy was often the victim of unfair jokes as he hobbled along with a scarred cane and untold stories of his violent past. The only consolation to the misery of my day was that Joe, in a valiant last-minute effort to preserve at least part of my dignity, changed his mind about charging admission at the gate.

Luckily for me, Abby quickly came over soon afterwards to nurse not only my knee, but also my bruised ego. After stringing up my leg in a makeshift sling attached to the bedpost, she hovered nearby to cheerfully attend to my every need. It seemed like the perfect time to gather more information about my mother.

According to Abby, my mother had always been the Life of the Party. The two girls would alternate white gloves and party dresses with their tennis whites, to woo the boys of the Forties with their incredible style.

"Caroline had a very mischievous side," Abby said with a grin, "which could always be counted on to shake things up just when our lives were becoming a little too mundane." These would be the occasions when they would select a place on the map, and, ignoring Society Women's Rules of the Day, defiantly venture off on their next journey.

"But where did you get the money?" I asked suspiciously.

"Oh, we had summer jobs at The Iroquois Hotel in Mackinac Island," she replied, explaining that the Rich and Famous were just discovering this quiet haven of Michigan's Upper Peninsula, and there were always invitations that included a summer home to stay in.

"But the Big Dream that had us saving all our summer wages," Abby added, "was our determination to visit the great frontier of Alaska."

Abby said the quest to develop this rugged, mysterious land had lured single men from all over the country. "According to our mothers, the pickings were becoming pretty slim at our age," she said with a playful wink, "And rightly so, since we were both nearing the ripe old age of twenty-six. Therefore, we were convinced that the odds were stacked in our favor to find both adventure and romance in Alaska. It was 1953, I think, when your mother and I set sail by way of the Inside Passage."

"What?" I cried. "Were you and my mom a couple of Run-A-Ways?"

Abby shook her head. "As fortune would have it," she continued, "your mother's brother, Uncle George, had recently moved to Anchorage, so we planned to stay with him until we could find proper jobs."

"So, how did my mom and dad meet?" I persisted.

"Carolyn found work as a registered nurse at a hospital in Anchorage," Abby replied. "And, as fate would have it, your father, a local bush pilot, was admitted as a patient for one of his notorious daredevil tactics. Now, your father" she sighed as if she were back in Alaska, reliving this Big Romance, "was a dashingly handsome voyager. Many girls had tried and failed to gain his attention, but your mother was the one and only woman who made him stop in his tracks and take notice."

"If God had arranged for this meeting to happen clear across the continent," I confided to Abby, "He must have hired a whole slew of angels in order to get my parents there on time!"

"I'm sure he did indeed!" Abby chuckled, and then went on to give me the Rest Of The Dirt. "After serving in the Navy and becoming one of the few survivors of *The Californian* during Pearl Harbor, Bill attended The Spartan School of Aeronautics, and immediately began flying with a group of young Bush Pilots who were bent on taming what was still only a territory of the United States. These men traveled in packs, bound together by their love of flying the world's first small Cessna's." Abby's eyes suddenly took on a faraway glint. "Oh, my, the stories those pilots told!" she laughed.

"What stories, Abby?" I asked, captivated.

"Oh, I'll tell you a few when you're older," she answered carefully. "But you have every reason to be proud of your father. These men trapped and fished on the tip of Alaska's most brutal areas, charting undiscovered lands with a spirit that could only be compared to today's astronauts," she said, her eyes glowing with admiration.

"In love with your mother's beauty, intelligence and startling sense of humor," Abby declared, "Bill vowed that this was one woman for whom he would be willing to sacrifice his other great devotion—that of his beloved Alaska. I remember your dad's friends were completely bewildered," she concluded with a little smile of victory for her Best Friend's achievement in capturing this elusive man. "At twenty-seven, your father already had the reputation of a confirmed bachelor. But eventually, his friends gave in and blessed this new romance that was quickly forming into a lifetime love."

"I don't know, Aunt Abby . . . it seems to me that Alaska was an awful long way to go just to pick up a couple of husbands."

"Sometimes, honey, we do things that do not always make much sense as we get older. In your mother's case," she added with a brilliant smile, "she did indeed find her destiny waiting for her."

As it turned out, Abby had decided to go back to her hometown, where her own Destiny was patiently waiting for her return from The Great Alaska Adventure. She married her High School Sweetheart, who happened to live next door!

On the final day of my recovery, I reviewed my notes and sauntered back into the world with a new understanding of my mother. Meanwhile, taking advantage of my crippled state, my brother had done his best to claim my allowance from my father, since I had lost the earlier staircase bet. After a very convincing argument from Joe, my father wearily declined his request. I knew my situation must have been pretty grave, because my father was usually very firm about Paying Your Dues.

"HAPPY BIRTHDAY TO YOOOOU! HAPPY BIRTHDAY TO YOOOOU!" sang my siblings with exaggerated force, oblivious to being off-key in their quest to humiliate me. Patiently enduring the rotating cake platter that was strictly reserved for commemorating these embarrassing events, I successfully blew out each of my eight candles with the proper enthusiasm. Inside, however, I was anxious to escape back to the Big Family Secret that was hiding in the attic at that very moment.

After using the bread box to hoist herself up, Theresa, the youngest, was busy scrambling across the kitchen countertops in search of her favorite chipped plate and a glass of milk. At six-years-old, she was already learning to fend for herself. I admired my little sister's determination, and laughed when my father pretended to have eaten her share of cake during her short absence.

"Dad . . . !" she cried as he scooped her up in his lap to hug her tightly.

"You are my Duke of all Dukes," he told her. My father had unusual endearments for us all.

As the group settled down, he handed me a large, brightly colored gift containing a new Chemistry Set. All my accumulations of Grace, carefully completed Penances, and many Acts of Contrition, had not, it seemed, produced a Red Radio Flyer. Nevertheless, from the look of obvious yearning on Joe's face, this was certainly a nice Consolation Prize.

I decided that riding Joe's new blue Schwinn bike would be a fair trade for the use of the chemistry set—even though the last time I rode it, my feet had slipped off the pedals, causing me to slide off the banana seat onto the Boys Bar. With fresh tears in my eyes and an excruciating pain in my groin area, I had stumbled blindly back home and returned the evil contraption to Joe, who explained that this bar was purposely installed on *all* boys' bikes to prevent Little Sisters from ever riding them again.

Now, studying the words "For Ages Eight and Up," I knew without a doubt that I had achieved Big Kids Status. I sashayed past Joe, who seemed appropriately peeved, with a wink that was sure to arouse his animosity even further.

Claiming my one and only annual opportunity to be excused from washing the dishes, I gave my father a grateful kiss and headed back up to the attic with a larger-than-average piece of chocolate cake. But first, I stopped by my mother's bedroom, where she was once again "Resting" and quietly slipped a pearl studded comb into my pocket. She never even noticed.

At this point in my research, I had begun sharing my attic space with Jean's best friend, Cathy McNamara. Her own mother had recently been hospitalized with Cancer: an illness that Cathy felt sure came from the many beatings that her mother had endured from Cathy's father over the years.

Cathy, a blonde, lanky girl with hair of pure spun straw, was known for her relentless pranks and the amazing gift of using her long toes to produce agonizing pinches to your legs. She was also famous in our family for her uncanny ability to break valuable objects by merely looking at them. The day Cathy broke my favorite Topo Gigio bank just by picking it up and shaking the coins, I told her she had The Curse, which were the only words that ever seemed to hurt her feelings. I made a mental note then and there to use that weapon again—but only if it was well deserved.

Last month, Mr. McNamara woke up with an excruciating headache and an empty bottle of Scotch, and then stumbled off in search of "the fellah who owes me a drink." After a few days of their father's absence, during which time the McNamara home was more peaceful than it had been in years, Cathy and her little brother Casey decided that they would simply have to Fend For Themselves.

Even though Casey was only six-years-old, Cathy had felt that he was handling his role as Man of The House rather nicely. Like *Hansel and Gretel,* the two siblings might have gone on this way forever, if only they had not been caught Red-Handed when they attempted to purchase a Tonka Truck for Casey with the Food Stamps that had been discovered in their mother's dresser drawer.

Ruthie, the bug-eyed clerk at Fabiano's Corner Store, had seized both the toy truck and the chocolate doughnuts and rushed them to the Authorities as evidence, which had resulted in an immediate raid on the short-lived serenity of the McNamara house. Casey, who politely asked the Authorities if they were interested in some Macaroni and Cheese, was just setting the table for dinner when he was whisked out of his home like a Common Criminal.

Luckily, Cathy was busy hanging out with a group of kickball players at the time. It was only after arriving home to find strange men rummaging through the kitchen that she had the amazing forethought to escape through a back cornfield. Jean and Lisa were braiding each other's hair when they heard the hollering from below their bedroom window. Joe was nice enough to help haul the shaking Cathy safely up the entire two stories, using the pretty embroidered sheets that were tucked clear in the back of my mother's linen closet.

It was Jean who overheard Ruthie smugly announce to basically any Fabiano customer who would listen, that Casey was being held in a Foster Home until relatives could be found. In the meantime, there had been a unanimous agreement that we siblings would not purchase any of our candy at Fabianos' for at least one month, and instead we would walk the extra three blocks to Pasiano's—just to show out support.

My sisters had also made the delightful decision to hide Cathy in our attic. It was to be a Big Secret, Lisa and Jean had confided. Not even my dad would know that we were doing Cathy a great favor by hiding her from The Authorities, who would surely take her away if they discovered her whereabouts. They had thought long and hard about sharing the secret with Theresa and me but had finally decided that this time we were old enough to understand.

It was only when the consequences of Spilling The Beans were more clearly spelled out however, that Theresa and I made an even stronger resolution to Keep A Zipper On It. After all, it would not be much fun to be dangled from the window of the attic while Joe tickled the bottoms of our feet. Even now, the long feather that was taped near the window served as a constant threat of the Chinese Torture that would be instilled, should we ever forget to keep the Big Secret to ourselves.

We children were all doing our part by stashing our leftovers into napkins to sneak up to Cathy after dinner. I felt bad about giving her my brussel sprouts, but tried to make up for it by offering up more than half of my dessert as an Act of Contrition. In return, Cathy was assisting me with my research notes. All in all, it seemed like a fair arrangement.

I usually tried to steer clear of Cathy and Jean whenever they got together, because they were just like Cinderella's Two Wicked Stepsisters. When Cathy was alone, however, she would be my friend. Today, she was pleased to see the Birthday Cake, which seemed like an appropriate symbol for our newfound truce.

Cathy seemed excited as she rushed me up the stairs and into The Attic. "You will never guess what happened today!" she exclaimed with a mischievous grin.

After a successful two weeks as an Outlaw, there had been a close call for Cathy that morning while the rest of us were in school. Our housekeeper, Marilyn, flourishing a large dust mop along with her usual Bad Attitude, had decided to do a more-thorough-than-usual cleaning in the attic. Slinking back into the dark corners, amid cobwebs and unseen varmints, Cathy watched in horror as the dust mop actually swept across her shoes. However, we were lucky this time because Marilyn's vision was Not What It Used To Be.

To make matters worse, my mother had also walked past Cathy in the middle of the night as they were both making their way to the bathroom. The Coast Was Clear, however, since my mother had not even noticed. Brushing past her in the darkened hallway, she had simply murmured "Goodnight Dear," as if Cathy were just another daughter.

"It's just like I was *invisible!*" Cathy was saying, biting hungrily into the cake.

As she said those words, I realized that I too was beginning to understand the feeling of being invisible to my mother.

"Well, just try to stay out of the way," I said. "I'll give you one of the blankets off my bed. And see if you can wait until morning to use the bathroom. If you can't, you can always use that," I offered with a grin, pointing to an old abandoned paint pail.

"The day *that* happens, I'm turning myself in!" Cathy shot back.

Using her loads of spare time, Cathy had neatly arranged the little piles of Love Letters that made up our most exciting discovery in the attic so far. Still tied with pale blue ribbon and stacked in chronological order, the letters picked up the story of my parents' romance where Abby had left off.

My grandmother, it seemed, was not about to let her youngest daughter be taken hostage by "one of those wild young pilots of Alaska," and after many tears and letters of protest, had eventually convinced my mother to return home from Anchorage. But this rebellious love still survived in the form of letters marked with curious stamps and signs of wear from eager openings. Having traveled thousands of miles between Anchorage and my mother's home in Michigan, the words seemed to leap off the pages with joy and anticipation for the future that my parents had committed to share.

My father's letters were filled with his usual good humor, courting my mother with tales of his great Alaskan Adventures.

"Why, just this morning," he had written in one note with what appeared to be a more unsteady hand than usual, "I woke up to what I thought was certainly the largest earthquake we've ever encountered in Alaska. When the trembling stopped, I struggled across the shaking floor to grab my rifle," he boasted, "just in time to witness a huge Grizzly ambling away." Apparently, the old bear had decided to use my father's cabin to scratch an itch on his back, blissfully unaware of his own towering strength.

Before that year was over, my mother must have decided to just Throw Caution To The Wind and sail back to Alaska. My father, of course, was patiently waiting for his bride-to-be, as if there had never been any question of her return.

When my parents announced their sudden wedding, the news was not received as warmly as they had hoped. In her letters, my grandmother seemed disappointed about a marriage that would take her youngest daughter so far away from her hometown. On top of that, my father was a farmer's son from a small town called St. Cloud, Minnesota and did not share my mother's social class or her extended education.

"What's worse," my mother confided in a letter to her sister, Mary Jane, "is the fact that Bill is of German descent."

My grandmother, who prided herself on being a Navarre, a direct descendant of the French Royal Family, had challenged this relationship from the beginning, but to no avail. Carolyn was charmed by this romantic adventurer, and her siblings agreed that they had never seen their youngest sister look so happy as she began her new life in my father's rustic log cabin.

"The cabin is small and very remote, but it's gradually coming along," my mother wrote in a pretty, lavender-scented note addressed to Abby, "This place is really in need of a woman's touch, and some good old-fashioned elbow grease. The good news is that we've agreed to have scads of children," she added. "After all, two suppressed Catholic lovers have to make up for lost time!"

I dropped the letter in my lap, realizing with a growing horror what my mother was hinting at: Sex was really Housework in disguise. This theory, however, seemed much more acceptable than the way Sex had been described to me by Jean and Cathy; I simply could not conjure up the image of being born in a Test Tube with doctors having to spend days molding my head together like Play-Doh.

"If we all come from The Woman's Touch," I asked, frowning at Cathy, "how in the world do we get poured into The Test Tube?"

"Simple," she stated rather haughtily, "The Milkman puts The Test Tube into a bottle of chocolate milk and then drops us off on the back porch with his weekly delivery." I shot Cathy an admiring glance and shook my head. She had the answer to everything.

As a Bush Pilot, my father was required to spend weeks flying through some of the most primitive areas of Alaska, including a little spot in the farthest point north of the State called Point Barrow. During this time, my mother wrote that she frequently came down with some illness called, "Cabin Fever." Apparently, the bug would miraculously disappear when my father returned home from his journeys. It seemed however, that my mother was consoled during these lonely periods by the many friends and family who offered both companionship and supplies.

Cathy and I thought my mother must have been highly courageous to pack up and head to the frigid Arctic like that, just for the sake of one man. We decided that if our housekeeper Marilyn ever discovered Cathy, packing her as a Stowaway on an airplane to Alaska might be a solution to our problems. "If we're going to have to find you a husband in Alaska," I said, handing her the comb from my mother's vanity, "you might want to start by combing your hair."

The long, cold Anchorage winters had, quite rapidly it appeared, produced the first of the Peters Children. After calculating the numbers, I was disappointed to find that Lisa was indeed not Born Out Of Wedlock. (Lisa was fond of throwing shoes at all of us during her Temper Tantrums, and this fact would have made perfect artillery.)

Nevertheless, in August of 1954, a baby with blonde curly locks and wide blue eyes was brought into the circle of friends with much aplomb and plenty of cigars distributed by an adoring father. Underneath the newborn picture, which stuck out from among the overflowing memoirs of Lisa Marie's pink silk Baby Book, my father's neat handwriting proudly marched across the page with the words, "Now, THAT'S a Baby."

Meanwhile, I couldn't help noticing that even though I searched each box carefully, the beautiful pastel album that was supposed to record MY birth was nowhere to be found. Obviously, the marvel of having a baby had Worn Out Its Welcome the fourth time around.

Anyway, at just three months old, Lisa was already the Apple Of My Mother's Eye. "Today, Lisa was introduced into the Alaska Territory by the Pilots of Alaska in their own unique fashion," my mother gushed. "The men created a sled out of an old Borax soap crate, and surrounded the box with pillows and blankets. Lisa was hitched to the team of dogs, and escorted through the Alaskan wilderness for the sleigh ride of her life. She adored every minute of it!"

Cathy and I concluded that there must have been a lot of Housekeeping to be done after that, because The Woman's Touch delivered Jean, Joe, and me into the world within three short years.

"It is so sweet to watch Bill inspecting each of their tiny toes and fingers," my mother wrote in a journal entry. "He is filled with wonder at each new arrival, claiming that the miracle of birth is even more mysterious than the miracle of flight that still overcomes him each time the Cessna rises majestically off the ground."

It was obvious that my mother must have had her hands full with all those babies, since the pile of letters became smaller after my arrival. A faint whiff of milk seeped through the perfumed, gilded envelopes as the precise handwriting of earlier entries turned into hurried scrawls on yellow legal pads—the matching stationery now just a reckless luxury.

Meanwhile, my father was busy basking in the Joys Of Fatherhood. Like a young lover, he was discovering Alaska with whole new eyes, as was evident in one rather poetic journal entry:

"The dark winter days gradually grow longer until finally, in a glorious display of rebellion, offer up to twenty-three hours of summer daylight, while the northern lights cast a luminous shine on our small cabin. These are the exquisite moments that unveil the treasures of Alaska like a surreal gift to those who risk her perils. Not unlike the guarded mistress, for whom one must risk danger in order to secretly revel in her beauty."

It would be a whole year later, in a letter postmarked 4/2/56, before my mother had a chance to record this exciting new entry in her own journal: "There has been an answer to our persistent requests to obtain schooling for the growing number of Catholic elementary children in Anchorage," she wrote with enthusiasm. "A tiny schoolhouse discovered on the outskirts of the village is finally going to be given to us by county officials." My parents seemed to find an exciting Common Ground as they volunteered their time to create the first Catholic school in Anchorage, Alaska.

"As I continue to teach and Bill pursues his passion for flying, life is at once serene and guarded in this primitive wonderland. The children are all with me during the school day. My life feels so complete."

Finally, Cathy and I discovered A Turning Point that would bring those Mystical Moments my parents had shared in Alaska to a close. "Bill has been diagnosed with Diabetes," my mother wrote, "and it is with great sadness that he has been forced to resign his pilot's license." But there was better news to come, I read with a sigh of relief. "A position has been offered to him at an Aeronautical Plant in Southern California. There have been many tears shed, since we must reluctantly say goodbye to the children of St. Francis School."

"This has been a very emotional time for the both of us," my mother continued. "As the Bush Pilots of Alaska stood by, Bill was saluted by these friends who had been his comrades in the Bush for more than twenty-four years."

After sharing a lifetime of experiences together, my father had been recognized by his fellow pilots for his contributions to the settlement of this new frontier. It all seemed very honorable, and a renewed love for my daddy bubbled up in my chest when I wondered whatever happened to all his friends.

It was in a letter postmarked 1959, that my mother first described the impact of Alaska's new Statehood into America. "This news," she wrote, "has been received with great despair by the Alaskan bush pilots, who are forecasting the demise of this beautiful country that they have painstakingly discovered and protected like a beloved stepchild."

"In truth, I think that Bill is ready to thaw out from all those years of Alaska adventures," she continued. "Although this remote land offered him a cocoon of safety from his ravaged memories of Pearl Harbor, we're looking forward to the warmth of the California sun."

"Maybe," she added with more than a glimmer of hope, "its welcoming sunlight will mean warm new beginnings for our family. God only knows we could use them . . ."

While studying the photographs of our California home, I could recall certain details that zoomed in and out of focus like my father's old leather-bound camera. The house was Spanish-style white stucco with an enclosed patio that housed the many bushels of fruits picked from our apricot, avocado, and tangerine trees. Theresa was born in California and the Christmas photos that year showed five happy children, all dressed up for Santa Claus in matching red outfits.

"My mother was feeling good during those years," I explained to Cathy, my memory struggling to flash on happier days.

If I really concentrated on those days, I could still hear my mother's beautiful, comforting voice as she placed my hands into hers for the dance that was reserved just for us. After inserting an album into the mysterious brown box called a hi-fi, we would waltz and sing with wild abandon to the tunes of Doris Day:

Que Sera Sera
Whatever will be, will be
The future's not ours to see
Que Sera Sera

Then laughing, we would fall onto the sofa together for some private cuddle time. While smoothing the unmanageable bump in my hair that a Cow Once Licked, my mother would often murmur, "Oh, Annie. You are my pearl of great price." As if I were her only child in the world.

That evening, Theresa and I thumped our usual good night to Cathy on the left corner of my bedroom ceiling. Satisfied to hear the rat-a-tat of her response, I snuggled into bed and continued to let my mind drift back to the Normal Times that our family had shared in California. I remembered that every Saturday evening my mother would call us together from her green damask chair in the Piano Room. With rosaries in hand and wearing our Best Behavior, all five of us would make our way through the literature, macramé needles, and partially graded papers to kneel around my mother in a circle.

Fingering each of the tiny blue jewels leading up to the cross that seemed a lifetime away, I would often let my eyes wander to this lovely person who resembled a matriarchal queen. My mother's soft blue eyes and glowing olive skin were complemented by a shiny mass of brown curls, usually swept up into a perfect French twist. Her smile could visibly light up the room with a love that seemed especially reserved for each one of us alone. As we prayed aloud in unison, it wasn't hard to envision that we were angels at the feet of the Virgin Mary herself.

My father, arriving home for the evening, would quietly peek at this scene with an expression of contentment. As we all peered back through half-open eyes, he would wink at us and quietly begin to close the door.

"Amen-Hi-Daddy!" we would recite in one ecstatic breath, knowing that the permission to end Prayer Time would be granted immediately. All of us children would chatter uncontrollably with my father while he escorted my mother toward the warm smells of spicy chili on the stove. Our family was happy and, well . . . together. And try as I might, this was the last real togetherness I was able to remember.

3

December 1964

"What do you think is wrong with Mom?" I asked Joe as we carefully picked our way around a patch of ice. The fresh road salt was forming a gray mushy consistency with the crusty snow, in sharp contrast to yesterday's picture-perfect snowfall. I was careful not to scuff my new red boots; a gift that had come as a complete surprise from my father, who had seen the longing in my eyes every time we walked past the Knapp's department store window. I had also received new slippers, robe, and underwear, and it wasn't even Christmas yet. My suspicions were definitely aroused; something was up.

Lumbering along with his hands in his pockets Joe mumbled a response that signaled he did not want to discuss the subject. I sighed at his reaction, even though I was learning that it was the nature of men to unveil information only at their convenience.

At only eight-years-old, my brother was almost five feet tall, and it was always fun to watch the crowd part as they made way for him on the basketball court. Because Joe and I shared the same grade, I was blessed with a Lifelong Bodyguard. (Although in later years, with much hesitation, he allowed me occasional dates with all of the same boys he had been protecting me from.)

A master of negotiations, Joe made it seem like he was offering me a promotion when he made me his Newspaper Route Assistant for three months. Balancing myself on the cold handlebars of his bike, I became quite adept at cutting my wrist just so-for perfectly targeting a porch. I did, however, draw the line at ringing a door-bell to collect for the week's paper. Blushing, I would hide in the bushes until the whole uncomfortable ordeal of begging was over and the people could go back to eating their dinner.

For the most part, I was proud of my brother's intelligence; although I was still stinging from the time he allowed me to copy his math homework—and then later changed all his answers to the right ones.

But right now, I was on Joe's good side, and really did not want to Press My Luck. It was only because of the well-meaning church members who were suddenly dropping in to assist with dinner and chores that I felt the need to pry.

Since it was uncommon for fathers to take care of their children by themselves, the Catholic Charities Organization had recently stepped in with its own solution. The atmosphere in our home was becoming more and more ominous with each closed-door discussion that was held in the Piano Room.

In fact, only yesterday, we were each given fifty cents for a

Sunday matinee at the theater. Typically, this rare treat was only observed when my parents were making Google Eyes at each other and needed to be alone.

The movie we had chosen was the magical new release, *Mary Poppins*. I fervently tried to imagine our former housekeeper, Mildred, as the enchanting nanny who arrived by umbrella to sprinkle our home with music and laughter. But it wasn't easy, because *our* nanny was a stoic German woman with calloused hands, a greasy knot of hair, and tasteless, faded Muumuus that must have come straight off the rack at the Salvation Army store. Also, Mildred preferred to poison all the pigeons instead of singing to them sweetly like Mary Poppins did in the film.

In addition to all her other unique characteristics, Mildred had the uncanny ability to twist her personality into extremes that often resembled those of *Dr. Jekyll and Mr. Hyde*. After sweetly assuring my father that our ultimate care was her only priority, she would suddenly whirl on us with all the vengeance of a vicious shrew after he walked out the door. You had to hand it to The Prude; it was truly an Oscar-winning performance.

Tragically, I had received my one and only spanking from the cranky old woman, strictly for drawing a stunning, six-foot-tall Hawaiian girl across my bedroom wall.

This traumatizing experience had occurred after a particularly bad breakfast of leathery oatmeal that was missing all the right ingredients like raisins and cinnamon. It was only after Joe had convinced me that Mildred had "laced our gruel with poison," that I decided to slip away to my bedroom, unnoticed.

I went right to work for what was to be the most enlightening masterpiece of my artist's career. First, I created a makeshift scaffold from my top bunk order in order to obtain just the right vantage point. Then after much deliberation, I finally settled on the perfect palette from my rare collection of colored chalks. A few painstaking hours later, Mildred burst onto the scene–strictly uninvited–and that was when the rude interrogation began.

At the time, I was busy delivering the last minute touches to the toes of the Hawaiian girl with a bottle of Avon nail polish that was aptly named *Hawaiian Petal.* Because, the Avon Representative has assured my mother in a hushed tone that this color was "All The Rage" at the local university, I also used the polish to sign and number my work.

Obviously, I was more surprised than anyone when my back-breaking efforts resulted in a spanking on my bed, while Ginger, The Hawaiian Girl, looked on with an unmistakable look of compassion for my dilemma. This Invasion Of Privacy had come as a complete shock not only to me, but also to my father when I quietly informed him of the Great Injustice. My dad had given Mildred a dreadful talking-to for breaking the very strict rule of No Punishment At Home, and I just knew that there would be Hell To Pay from old Mildred when she discovered that I had turned her in.

The following weekend, I did my best not to preen when my mother came home from her latest Slumber Party and, with a voice that sounded more tired than usual, reassured me that my Hawaiian girl was "a beautiful work of art." Then to my complete surprise, she said that I would be allowed to keep it on the wall Until Further Notice. We even did a hula dance together before she tucked me into bed that evening. This little victory was somewhat tarnished, however, when Mildred made a point of sneering at my masterpiece every time she made the bunk bed. I began to think my mother was right: Mildred was just plain jealous of my budding talent.

And then, Straight Out Of The Blue, on a recent bitterly cold afternoon, God shed a Miracle on our family . . . It was while engrossed in her usual medley of Soap Operas, that Mildred had locked all of us children out of the house. This was a common occurrence with our housekeeper, but I imagined that within the magic "Hush" potion that was disguised as Hot Chocolate, we had been brainwashed into not sharing this information with others.

Anyway, that afternoon, we had exhausted all our usual outdoor winter activities: tobogganing down Dead Man's Hill, climbing up the roof of the garage only to slide down the frozen willow tree straight into a pile of snow, and even gathering old vegetable and fruit cans to store in the cabinets of our newly remodeled snow igloos. Periodically, someone would knock on the door to let Mildred know that we were becoming increasingly cold and wanted to come in, only to receive a harsh grunt in response.

It was only when Lisa was issuing the rewards for Most Creative Snow Igloo, that we realized Mildred was simply not going to let us back in the house at all. I looked hopefully at my brother for a glimmer of leadership. Joe, aware that all eyes were on him, sighed and announced in a matter-of-fact tone that this time, we were going to Freeze To Death. This rude awakening led Theresa (who, for being the youngest, had an amazingly strong set of lungs) to bawl uncontrollably.

Jean immediately fled back to her snow igloo to try to salvage any remnants of food that might be found at the bottom of the cans. I, in turn, dropped promptly to my knees with fervent Hail Mary's–if only to stop the vision of the five of us limping around the back yard with tattered clothing around our haggard skin just like the Holocaust Victims. Lisa, exasperated with us all, had a final strategy that as it turned out worked entirely in our favor.

It was Rita Gonzalez, our compassionate next-door neighbor, who finally heard the collective howls of protest as we stomped our frozen feet and rebelled with unanimous cries of "HELP!" Ultimately, Mildred, wearing her familiar scorn and a very unattractive cow print, allowed us back inside, but only after the obvious bribe of a warm peanut butter cookie was thrust into the hands of Rita Gonzalez.

My father's discovery of *this* event from the concerned neighbor had earned old Mildred an immediate pink slip and a formal escort into a yellow-and-black checkered taxicab. We children cheered from the safety of the attic window, while Mildred looked up at all of us, pink curlers still in her hair, wearing a look of pure disgust. Later, while warming my numb toes in front of the heat register, I marveled at the fact that as a force, the greatest single asset that the Peter's Children possessed was our steady strength in numbers.

"Joe-y, what do you think is wrong with Mom?" I persisted, panting to keep up with the quick strides of his endlessly long legs. "When they say she is sick, does that mean she has the flu?"

Just when it appeared that his lips were moving in the positive direction of a response, I heard the pounding of feet behind me.

"Run!" My brother yelled.

I turned around to look just as The Tomanica Brothers seized Joe by the collar of his crisp white shirt. Larry—the oldest and certainly the most vicious of this family of bullies—already had my brother pinned up against the red brick wall of the alley, grasping him by his Saint Mary's School navy-blue tie in a strangled hold. Joe's eyes looked as if they were going to bulge right out of their sockets.

"Go get help," Joe whispered from the side of his mouth. Contemplating the situation, I realized that Joe would be a bloody pulp if I wasted any time finding assistance. Besides, since our house was very quiet these days, the odds of finding any available military aid were not stacked in my favor.

"Larry Tomanica, you let go of my brother!" I yelled.

When Tommy and Mikey just smirked at me, the pressure suddenly seemed too much to bear. I tore into Larry with all the anger of a child who is dealing with the first-hand knowledge of an Unfair World, savagely kicking, spitting, and hitting him until even the other two brothers stood by in awe of the rage emerging from my small frame.

Finally, my vengeance seemed to make a dent as Larry let go of Joe to massage his bruising ankle. Joe took this opportunity to give Larry one last pop in the arm; as if to reclaim his manhood from the appreciative glances that I was now receiving from The Tomanica Brothers.

After brushing the cooties off my beloved red boots and silently thanking them for their magical protection from the Enemy, I continued home with my brother. We both agreed to avoid the usual alleys that contained the perils of bullies in favor of The Long Way, since Joe admitted that he was just plain tuckered from tackling all the Tomanica Brothers barehanded.

"Mom's got Mental Illness," Joe finally offered.

"What's Mental Illness?" I asked.

"It's not good," he responded.

"Oh," I said, grateful for any information. As I looked up into the star-encrusted sky, my warm breath formed a soft white halo that hovered for just a moment before evaporating into an eternal blanket of cobalt-blue. Just then, an icy snowball whistled past my left ear. As we sprinted toward 721 Michigan Avenue, the words of the familiar challenge, "I'll Beat You Home!" sailed with a disturbing echo through the swirling branches of the newly exposed maple trees.

4

January 1965

I f I paid very close attention, I could almost see the outline of Old Man Winter's cheeks as he blew impish puffs of cold air that soared through the cracked classroom window–causing Sister Josetta's paperwork to stir from her desk with quiet discontent. Just as I was uttering a fierce prayer that *my* homework would be chosen to mysteriously rise out that window, there was a quiet Miracle, as a final gust from the grinning cloud upset the agonizingly tedious afternoon. The Front-Row- Brown–Nosed- Students, (as Joe referred to them), scurried over each other to retrieve the flurry of math papers, and then to my complete disgust, *curtsied* to the rigid nun. The rest of us tried not to appear envious; after all, this rare opportunity would almost guarantee the Brown Nosers at least a Thimbleful Of Grace for the noble act of redeeming Sister Josetta's day. On one momentous occasion, it was said, there was actually a Barrel Full of Grace issued to one outstanding altar boy who single-handedly caught Father Fedewa as he swayed forward from the altar after a particularly healthy swig of wine from the large golden goblet. I stopped to consider that my Grace points were sinking dangerously low by comparison, and briefly wondered what excuse I would need to keep my Foot In The Door when I finally got to Heaven.

The triangle-shaped note landed safely at my feet, and I bent over to pick it up just as Sister Marie Josetta turned back to the blackboard. Joe grinned at me from the next aisle over, and I shot him a dirty look for his carelessness in timing. Everyone knew that Passing Notes could easily earn you the humiliation of pushing a peanut down the classroom aisle with your nose.

Deciphering the large scrawls of my brother's bad penmanship, I learned that an Urgent Family Meeting had been called on the playground of St. Mary's that day. Apparently, Sister Superior had called Lisa and Jean into The Principal's Office to inquire if they had seen Cathy recently. "They Are On To Us!!!!" he wrote.

I burst out into a cold sweat, wondering if Capital Punishment would be the fate of our whole family. I visualized us lumped together in chains, dragging a large black ball, destined to wear unflattering black-and-white garments for the Rest Of Our Lives. (Although with my thin frame, my mother had often mentioned that I wore stripes quite well.)

Lisa was larger-boned than the rest of us, with beautiful thick blonde hair, dreamy blue eyes that were often found drifting into her own more-colorful world, and a vivacious personality that perfectly matched the dark mole on her right cheek. Although her physical characteristics were closer to the German side of the family, Lisa had inherited the "living in the moment" mentality handed down from our French ancestors. A born leader and certainly the wisest of us all, Lisa was usually involved with playground activities that centered around her own popularity. When she broke away from her friends that day to gather her family together at the risk of her own reputation, we all knew the situation had to be pretty serious.

"Listen up, everyone," Lisa said, tossing her hair to one side. "It looks like Sister Superior suspects that we are hiding Cathy."

Watching her hands twitch nervously, I realized that this Little Incident would not prove to be favorable for Lisa's nomination as Sixth Grade Class President. Her bid for the upcoming election had been Neck To Neck for weeks with the popular Candy of the Well-To-Do O'Brien family. Flyers were posted everywhere on the red brick walls of the playground, pitting the two blondes against each other in a fierce competition. Yes, there was just too much to lose if The McNamara Kidnapping became a playground leak.

Lisa paced the alley of the schoolyard, clearly on the verge of tears. "Oh boy, are *we* in trouble now!"

I briefly tried to recall if I'd been part of the original decision to stuff Cathy in the attic, and decided to keep my mouth shut. After all, you didn't want to upset Lisa when she was in One Of Her Moods. Why, it was no secret that if you wanted to seek revenge on someone in our family, you simply arranged to push them into Lisa when she was reading on the couch. This act would almost guarantee a beating to the tormented victim - if Lisa were having a Bad Day. However, I had been considering that this year for Lent, I would "Give Up" abusing my little sister Theresa in this manner—instead of the usual candy sacrifice. This would mean, Father Franco had recently informed me during my last confession, that all the Grace Points I had lost that year, would go right back to The Grace Bank as if I never even spent them. No Questions Asked.

I brought my attention back to the schoolyard in time to witness

Lisa's eyes welling up with fresh tears of defeat—a sure sign that she was ready to blow. And then, just when I was considering that Candy O'Brien might get my vote if Lisa didn't change her attitude, my sister dropped her voice to the compassionate tone that was reserved for her siblings like a lion defending her cubs. "The Authorities are hot on our trail," she confided quietly, "and we are Cathy's only hope for survival."

That weekend, Lisa, Jean, Joe, and Theresa joined Cathy and me in the attic for a lunch of tuna fish sandwiches and Campbell's tomato soup. Lisa, with her usual sense of adventure, had made quite the game out of it. She was The Pretty Waitress, and the rest of us were merely The Happy Customers, except for Jean, who had somehow landed a leading role as The Pleasant Hostess (which, I had to admit, she was handling very nicely).

"Let me show you to your seats," Jean said with a little curtsy, ushering us to the table with a dramatic flourish.

I gasped with delight. Old milk crates had been transformed into elegant seating with little tulle skirts, delicately tied in back with pleated ivory bows. A rusty old tea table was dressed in one of the silk and lace dresses that my mother had once worn. For a centerpiece, my sister had found an old birdcage that was trimmed in green hydrangea from the garden, and real linen tablecloths were positioned into tiny tents on our paper plates. You had to hand it to her for creating a beautiful atmosphere out of an old attic. But then, "Jeannie has a flair for design," my mother always said.

Meanwhile, as Lisa daintily served us on T.V. Trays, complete with sterling silver napkin rings, we all knew our time together with Cathy was indeed becoming precious. Even my father, who had become accustomed to having Cathy around so often that she was just like another daughter, was getting suspicious.

After all the usual Passwords Of Secrecy, during which Lisa gravely held up The Feather as a symbolic reminder of its purpose, the meeting was underway. The first thing on the agenda was how we were going to get away with Telling A Fib, since we all knew that this was something my father would "simply not put up with." Lisa reminded us all that Jean had experienced this fact firsthand when she had once stolen a candy bar and lied to my father about where she had gotten it. Typically, she could Get Away With Murder, but my father had Seen Right Through It that day, and Jean received her one and only spanking.

"We leave the discipline to the nuns," I heard my mother remark rather proudly one evening as I was eavesdropping under the Bridge Table.

"Isn't that like throwing them to the wolves?" Mrs. Gallagher cackled while she dismantled her mink cape in order to take a sip of her martini. Fascinated, I observed the dead fox that served as a clasp to her cape now dangling within inches of my face—its beady little eyes mocking me for choosing such an obvious hiding place.

As I untangled my body from around the legs of the table to slink up to my bedroom unnoticed, the laughter all around confirmed that my parents did not fully realize the truth of that statement. Why, for the first semester of that year, Timothy Scott had received a brutal beating from Sister Theodore (known on the playground as Sister Ted), every morning after First Hour whether he needed it or not. Secretly, I wondered at her choice of career, since the towering frame of Sister Ted looked as if it would be more at home on a football field than in a convent.

We students would cringe whenever she blustered into the classroom. "Good Morning, Sister Theodore," we would sing, standing at attention beside our desks.

The sarcastic twang of our greeting was always answered with a simple, "You may sit down," the grim expression on her face suggesting that she had more pressing business to deal with than forty mocking students.

Sister Ted would then make a beeline toward Timothy, as if he were the sole target of all her frustrations. With clenched fists protecting his face, the wiry Timothy would face the brutal nun with his usual defiance, as if yesterday's brutality were simply not sufficient. "Keep your stinkin' hands off me, you witch," or something equally shocking would erupt from his pale, freckled lips.

Then, satisfied to have a reason for instilling Cruel And Unusual Punishment, Sister Ted would grab Timothy by the ears and slam him up against the chalkboard with an unearthly strength, shaking him by the thin blades of his shoulders until I feared his teeth would rattle right out of his head. Finally, brandishing a large wooden Paddle Board that mysteriously appeared from the folds of her gown, she would beat poor Timothy as we children helplessly looked on. Sister Ted's large, withered hand resembled a claw as it curled around the handle of the paddle. It was said arthritis had set in over the years . . . most likely from beating small children.

We knew to keep quiet, since each of us had felt the white heat of The Paddle on our knuckles at one time or another. Yes, it was best not to bring any attention to yourself when Sister Ted was present.

Now, with Lisa and Jean considering telling my father The Truth about Cathy that night after dinner, we were definitely pushing the No Punishment At Home rule to the limit. I had already planned to make myself a guest at The Wilson's' house for dinner until the whole thing had blown over. "I've been meaning to go to the library to work on my science project," said my cowardly brother, Joe.

Lisa gathered up our plates and stacked them in a corner. "The Dishwashers will clean these later," she said with assurance. Looking at each other, Theresa and I knew we had just been assigned our roles in the Restaurant game.

We all settled in to savor the ice cream sandwiches that my brother had contributed to the luncheon. Joe seemed Pleased As Punch that he could treat us girls with the money that had been earned from his newspaper route. He also seemed relieved to not have to put on one of my mother's silk gowns for the upcoming Fashion Show that day. The last time Joe had a modeling role, he complained of itching the whole time.

Cathy, the Guest of Honor, was expertly slurping the dripping vanilla ice cream from its chocolate sandwich. "I want to hear about The Great Kidnapping again," she said, anxious to steer the conversation away from herself.

By now, Cathy was very familiar with the story of our California home, which was centered smack in the foothills of Hollywood. She agreed that if it weren't for my grandmother bringing us to Michigan, we would all surely be part of *The Mouseketeers* by now.

As Lisa started to tell the story, I began to remember the details of leaving my father behind in California. A day that was still stamped in my mind just like a snapshot frozen in time, and ready to disturb my peace whenever I least expected it.

In 1962, when I must have been just five-years-old, we had an unexpected visit from my grandmother. Lurching up to the driveway in an old 1948 Chevrolet, "Gra" packed us up, and without so much as a word to my father, made the long treacherous drive across the country. Apparently, according to an entry that Cathy and I had just found in my mother's journal, Gra did not feel her daughter was being properly taken care of by her new husband. Personally, I don't think my mother was doing her best to put on A Happy Face.

As my siblings and I filed into the car like good little soldiers, there seemed to be an unspoken agreement among us that we were Not To Ask Questions. Our beloved California home quickly shrank to a small, still, speck as my mother backed out of the driveway. We were told there was a new life and home waiting for us in a town called Lansing, Michigan.

I wanted to scream that my daddy would not know our new address, but remained silent as Gra held me in her lap, and smoothing my hair, began to sing my favorite song:

I looked out the window and what did I see,
Popcorn Poppin' on the apricot tree.

I joined in the song with half-hearted enthusiasm, keeping my hand pressed into Jean's as a reminder that we were all to Keep Quiet.

It was only when we were driving on the winding road framed by the tall, ominous redwoods of Northern California that suddenly I was convinced *that Goldilocks and the Three Bears* were lurking behind those trees. The tension in the car seemed to break as everyone began to laugh at my "colorful imagination," but I was sure that the unknown territory my family was venturing into was as real as the gnarled black figures of the Redwoods that seemed to beckon us into their darkness. And then with a great sense of doom it hit me . . . I knew that we were heading for The Poor House—just as my mother had always feared.

The days of my mother's lilting voice, mingled with fresh starched sheets that swung in the jasmine-infused breezes, and backyard picnics consisting of tangy, squeezed orange juice with avocado sandwiches were lost forever with the For Sale sign that would be found posted that afternoon when my father came home from work.

Since he could not bear to be without us for even one day, my father immediately quit his job, and sold all of the household goods to reunite with his wife and children at 721 West Michigan Avenue.

Thus, a feud that would last a lifetime was hatched at that point between my father and his mother-in–law, their German and French backgrounds clashing as if it were World War II all over again. It made no sense to me. How could two people's love for one human being result in such dislike for each other?

In a daring attempt to Stir The Pot, I had begun to fancy myself as a CIA agent of sorts between my grandmother and father. It went something like this: With very little prompting, while lunching at Jacobson's, I would drop hints of a conversation I had overheard with my parents, and pass them on them to Gra.

"Grandma, daddy says you're a thievin' Son Of A Witch, and that your whole family is nothing but a bunch of Communists," I would recite with a serious expression.

At these times I could be assured of complete attention from the parties involved. Gra would place her silver fork down on her Limoges dessert plate and probe ever so gently, "Oh really, darling? What else does your father have to say?" At that point, I would begin to supply even more details, telling myself that even though some of it was invented, my father probably would have been thinking it, anyway.

Later on, I would sit on my father's lap and happily report not only the events of the day, but also the Very Important Information that I knew he would be looking forward to. "By the way, Daddy, Gra says you are a No-Good Kraut who will never amount to anything," I would solemnly inform him—and then I would lay my head on my fathers shoulder in true compassion for his circumstances. "Oh, really," my father would begin. "What else does your grandmother have to say about me?"

As I considered my latest tales of truth and fiction, it occurred to me that I just may have been building the largest Cardinal Sin ever. If I was lucky I would be banished to Purgatory forever. Worse, I could be driven straight down to Hell with no one but Hitler to hang out with—it made my skin tingle just to think about it . . .

"Well, I'm glad you ended up in Michigan," Cathy was saying, offering us all one of her rare crooked smiles. "Even though you would have made great *Mouseketeers,* those mouse ears would have been pretty uncomfortable after a while."

It would be many weeks later before I saw Cathy again on the playground at St. Mary's. Her new family had given her and her brother Real Bedrooms, complete with their own baths. Cathy had a new haircut and clothes that actually fit. Jean and Lisa were only slightly in trouble. My father said that he might have done the same thing If He Were In Their Shoes.

April 1965

I t was a beautiful spring afternoon, the last snowstorm having receded—although some bets were still on that there would be a final one before May. Glancing at my red Timex watch—a hand-me -down from Jean—I noted that it was exactly 3:15, and made the easy decision to take the short cut home from school. It was Wednesday, which was Baking Day at my grandmother's house. If my calculations were correct, I would be passing her house just in time to snag a warm chocolate-chip cookie.

I gingerly picked my way through Mr. Turner's prized rose garden, savoring the heady fragrance while keeping my eyes peeled.

Mr. Turner was known to mutilate little children for cutting through his garden, and just last week had chased Joe and Bill Kirby for a whole block with a loaded rifle just because they had tossed a cherry bomb into his rhubarb patch.

According to my brother's latest argument with Dad, the boys had no idea that the Turners' sleeping cat had selected that exact spot for his afternoon nap. The poor kitty had lost at least one inch of his tail, and I knew there was simply no Penance strong enough for hurting one of God's precious creatures. St. Peter himself would see to that when it came time for my brother to get through those Pearly Gates. Even Joe's most convincing arguments would fall on deaf ears, since St. Peter had probably heard it all by now.

For a moment, I pondered the fact that I might really miss Joe in Heaven. It was said that we close enough in age to be considered Irish Twins—and I was actually becoming quite fond of my brother.

Now finding myself at the back of my grandmother's property, I stopped to nibble on the first wild blueberries just beginning to ripen. As the sweet juice of the berry exploded on my tongue, I made a mental note to share this information with my siblings— but only after I had eaten more than my fair share.

Careful not to wipe my hands on my blue plaid uniform, I licked the tangy drops from my fingers and hitched up the scratchy, navy-blue knee socks that were forever slipping down to my ankles. The mouthwatering aroma wafting from my grandmother's kitchen seemed like an excellent reason to delay the homework assignments weighing on my back with all the heaviness of Sister Marie Rose's unplucked eyebrows.

"Hi Gra," I said, waving enthusiastically from outside her kitchen window.

"Oh, my," she responded with a large smile as I flaunted my

blueberry-stained fingers. "You don't suppose we could go pick enough of those berries for a pie, do you, dear?"

That was just like my grandmother to join in our activities, as if she were still a child herself. We grabbed the metal pail and skipped back to the blueberry bushes in perfect rhythm with each other.

Gra had plump rosy cheeks, light blue eyes, and a French bun that reminded me of a floating amber cloud. She wore silk dresses and interesting jewelry that held their own fascinating tales of travel and adventure. Her home was warm and toasty, filled with good things to eat. I relished the weekends of waking up in one of my grandmother's feather beds to the pleasant expressions of elegantly dressed porcelain dolls, and the smells of sizzling bacon and homemade strawberry jam.

We children especially loved to explore Gra's basement, where all the exotic treasures of her travels were packed away in tattered trunks that smelled of musky, faraway spices. Ancient furniture pieces that had never been finished as intended, grass skirts from Hawaii, and wooden masks served as perfect props for plays, offering hours of rainy-day playtime bliss.

Lounging to the tunes of *The Sound of Music*, I would pore over the latest fashion magazines that would magically appear on the bed in colorful harmony with the patchwork quilt. I loved to explore every detail of the latest clothes and makeup, and could always count on Gra to give me a liberated perspective on the styles of the day. The best part about weekends at Gra's was no church on Sunday morning!

I snuggled into my favorite down chair near the fireplace, savoring the news that Gra had shared with me during our berry-picking journey: There was to be a Magic Show that evening! Gra and I would be the Hosts of this special event and the rush of siblings and cousins would be arriving shortly. Rather than diving into the black satchel of homework that continued to glare at me from its forgotten corner, I decided to enjoy the private hour that would be all mine before the others arrived.

It was here in the reading corner, among shelves and shelves of dusty, faded books with worn bindings, that I could let my imagination take flight at any given time. The musty fragrance of old paper that drifted up from each book offered a sense of comfort that seemed to speak to me alone. Ancient fairy tales from printings over one hundred years old held penciled drawings of peculiar characters and beautiful people who had somehow found their way into some kind of A Pickle, but almost *always* resulted in A Happy Ending.

Once in a while, however, I would stumble on an exception to the standard happiness rule. The Little Match Girl, for instance, was a miserable tale that left me with an emptiness I could not explain. Why did someone not rescue this poor little girl from the cold? Didn't she know it was a Mortal Sin to be playing with matches? Limbo was her fate in the end—I was sure of it.

Scattered around the room were Gra's delightful old clocks that were collected from as far away as Switzerland and Germany. Small, large and medium clocks, some with stern and some with happy expressions, peeked out from among the books with an air of quiet companionship. Their synchronized ticking was interrupted every half-hour by a bright red bird that greeted me with a cheery "Coo-coo!" The Old Grandfather Clock was my favorite; I was sure that he was winking at me as if to say that his wisdom was superior to *all* those books combined.

I thought about my mother, who was once again staying on

The Fifth Floor at St. Lawrence Hospital. As her Slumber Parties became more frequent, I began to understand that Mental Illness meant that something was wrong with her mind. When my mother was home, all she did was pace back and forth while smoking cigarettes, unaware of anything around her. There was even talk that my mother may not be coming home for a few months this time.

Selecting *Little Black Sambo* from a corner shelf, I turned to a drawing of the persistent tigers who, exhausted from chasing each other tails, finally turned into a pool of butter. For a moment, I wondered how much time was left before my mother's mind, weary from chasing itself, would also give up, trading its torment for the idle comforts that were being offered by the People In The Other World.

Determined to Think Happy Thoughts, as Gra always instructed us, my stomach gave a little excited flip in anticipation of what lay ahead that evening. The Guest List included Gra's ever-expanding brood of grandchildren, which consisted of The Peters Children; the eleven offspring of my Aunt Mary, who were known as The Tripp Children; and the thirteen children of Uncle George, The Navarre Children. This night, the Invitation Only Event was to star the oldest Tripp, my cousin Johnny, who doubled as the All-Knowing Magician.

As I tried to keep up with the quick pace of my grandmother in order to get ready for the celebration, I pretended not to notice the cards, coins and tricks that were mysteriously brandished from what must have been Gra's own hiding places. Instead, I made myself busy scooping vanilla ice cream for the root beer floats that were to be distributed during intermission.

"Gra, what was Big Pa like?" I ventured, pleased to have the last few hours of Alone Time with her before all the competition decided to burst in.

"Oh, you would have loved Big Pa," Gra replied. He was full of mischief and surprises, and a very handsome man, at that."

After Gra's college graduation, she began at career at the Michigan State Highway Department. Apparently, my grandmother had a knack for securing all the right benefits, because shortly afterward she was awarded one of the first automobiles to roll off the exciting new Oldsmobile assembly line.

I studied the photograph of my grandparents in the kitchen that marked this historical introduction to The Horseless Carriage, and pitied the handsome, stern-looking man that would never know the joys of being a grandfather.

"How did he die?" I pressed rather daringly. After all, Gra was not known for discussing her private life openly.

"Well," she began, slowly sinking down into a large dining room chair while wringing her hands on a large cotton towel. "During World War I, when our government was looking for recruits into the Armed Forces, your grandpa felt that he should do the honor of serving his country. My sisters, Bee, Loretta, Georgie, and Dorothy, reluctantly said goodbye to their husbands, who were each called to active duty as well. It was only when all the men returned that we learned of something called 'Mustard Gas' because of the way it smelled. This poisonous gas, which seeped into the men's systems within hours of exposure, was known to cause painful blisters, blindness and death. Shortly after your mother's nineteenth birthday, she did indeed lose her father to this horrible poisonous gas."

"What!" I cried. "How come they never told us about that in history class?"

Gra suddenly seemed older than her already-ancient years as she wiped a corner of her eye with the towel. "Unfortunately, dear, there are some things that our government simply forgets to share with us," she said wearily.

"Well," I replied indignantly, scooping a last ball of still-frozen ice cream with a newfound earnestness, "You would think that our government would have gotten permission from the children of the United States before they accidentally lost all of our grandfathers to "Mustard Gas.""

Later that evening, I planned my debut in a little white number with pink lace that was especially chosen for the occasion. My grandmother had even permitted Just A Smudge of bright pink lipstick that tasted a bit like my Aunt Dorothy. This was not A Happy Thought, because Aunt Dorothy was the Spinster Of The Family with a face closely resembling a wrinkled prune, and knobby knees that peeked out from the confines of a silk dress that had seen far too many washings. It was said that Aunt Dorothy was a Gazillionaire, but you would never know it by the old newspapers which had accumulated near her fireplace for the last fifty years. "Did you know," I once overheard my Aunt Loretta crow to the other great aunts, "that Dorothy won't even subscribe to the paper anymore? Why she claims to have enough reading material to last her a lifetime!"

All I knew was that during one of the recent Racial Riots that had spread all the way from Detroit to Lansing's West Side, my mother fled to Toledo, Ohio with all of us children, and Aunt Dorothy had not exactly Welcomed Us With Open Arms. Instead, we were fed burnt toast with no jam as she made it clear that my mother was Acting Out Of The Ordinary. "All this talk of Riots is nothing but a bunch of rubbish," Aunt Dorothy admonished.

"I can assure you, there will be no uprising of the kind in little Lansing, Michigan."

But when we returned home that evening, the little shanties of homes that lined the Black People's Neighborhood, still reeked from the smoldering fires that had been spread in a quiet rage of rebellion. The acrid smoke burned my eyes as it crept stealthily through the lampposts like lingering shadows of forgotten spirits.

In the afterglow of a long cold winter, the porches of the shanties were usually filled with the thumping sounds of dancing feet and contagious spiritual songs, while little children of warm chocolate tones and many hair barrettes were rocked by cooing mothers. But that spring, just when the new daisies were pushing their eager little faces through the cracks of the confining sidewalk–the porches became eerily silent.

After our own Sunday services would end with a quick donut and a wave to the same old classmates, it was always a pleasure to drive past the courtyard of the Methodist Church. Jean and I took great delight in spying on the fashionably dressed All Black congregation - the women wearing elegant hats and an envious composure. But last Sunday Morning, it was obvious that the usual gaiety had been replaced with a new hardness to the eyes, while the men appeared to be clenching their fists.

"Its racial tension, honey," my father explained, as I once again tried to understand how something as simple as Skin Color would cause everyone to fight. But my father assured me that Martin Luther King was making big changes for the people in the shanties, and had even recently been awarded with The Nobel Peace Prize. I figured the Nobel Peace Prize must have been worth a whole planet full of Grace in Heaven.

Taking my place as Usher, I refused to allow Lisa and Jean into the doorway without first seeing their invitations. The jarring music of The Rolling Stones, which my father would not permit in our home, was pulsating loudly in the background just when The Big Announcement was made: During the second half of the show, my brother Joe would be Sawed In Two.

The delicious anticipation of this feat was almost better than the creamy brown suds that I was busy licking from the bottom of my A&W mug. I stopped to wonder which relative would have unknowingly taken the old mug from the window tray of this favorite Drive Up Restaurant, and decided in disgust that it was probably the same person who was responsible for the overdue library books in Gra's shelves that were still marked Property of Lansing Public Library: "Due Date: October 11th, 1934."

"Ladies and Gentlemen," Johnny boomed as he opened his large black cape to show us that he was not hiding any props, "we have here a very courageous boy who has agreed to risk his life for this Very Important Research that is about to be exposed to the world."

With a tip of his large black top hat, Johnny went on to point to my brother, who was lying quite serenely inside the wooden box.

"I, Johnny The Great Magician, will proceed to saw this young boy in half."

I eagerly leaned forward to get a better look and almost fell out of my chair in doing so. Wiping the suds from my new party dress, I happened to miss Johnny nudging the fake legs that had fallen out of the end of the wooden box. Everyone else, however, had already gotten a glimpse of the large pillow that had been stuffed with Joe's Levis, dirty socks, and black high-top Keds.

A rusty saw from the basement was produced, and with Jean, The Lovely Assistant, at his side, Johnny began to dutifully saw my brother in half. After only a few moments, a faint trickle of blood began to make its way through one of Joe's legs, giving way to a large bloody gash seeping through the rip in his jeans.

Suddenly, all the mean memories of my brother seemed to evaporate. Even the one where he tried to drown me in Lake Michigan wasn't so bad when I considered the possibility of Joe being confined to a wheelchair for the Rest Of His Life. Or worse, being buried in that very box since our family was not "in a position" as my father had recently confided, "to have anymore financial surprises."

The light from the candles that Gra had placed all around the living room "for atmosphere" began to flicker with a mad gaiety, as if Evil Spirits were celebrating their victory at my beloved brother's death.

"No!" I cried, brushing past my startled cousins and knocking down root beer floats in an effort to save my brother.

Johnny seemed amused. As his usual loud laugh took on an eerie howling sound, it seemed The Devil Himself was jeering at me.

With the kind of courage which can only come from pure terror, I ran to the box and yanked off the large silk scarf. And then, gasping with relief, I saw Joe's real legs all tucked up underneath—the stuffed pillow and fake blood merely an illusion.

With that, I promptly ran to the bathroom, crouched beside the toilet and threw up, hot tears of humiliation falling from my eyes.

"There, there, now," Gra soothed, pressing a cold towel to my forehead as I inspected the brown suds that were floating in the toilet with morbid fascination.

"They look like little Turkish soldiers wearing vanilla turbans on their heads," I observed out loud.

Gra laughed as she brushed my hair and changed my dress to a much less festive number, then brought me back out to the party with an expression that threatened anyone who dared to laugh at me. Johnny stooped down to pick me up and hold me his arms, smoothing down the layers of my ruffled dress while drying a forgotten tear from the corner of my eye.

"We're not going to hurt Joe," said Johnny, and I realized that the sneering grin had melted back into his slow, familiar smile.

As I surveyed the room, it seemed as if the haunting dance of the candles had come to an abrupt halt, now bathing the room with a soft tranquil blur of comforting light. *The Rolling Stones* had been replaced with the calm strumming of *Carole King,* and Joe was sitting upright in a comfortable position with no sign of blood whatsoever, his legs fully intact.

"Gosh, Annie, it's only magic," he said with a sheepish grin and playful punch.

"Well, I don't like magic," I shot back as I threw a pillow back at him, suddenly visualizing all the times that he had tried to smother me with pillows over my lifetime. "On second thought, I should have just let them saw you in half," I suggested.

Flaunting my ruffles with my head held high, I accepted the hot popcorn that was being handed to me by my cousin Donnie. But first, I was careful to pull out the large rubber worm that had been carefully buried under the sweet, buttery kernels of corn . . .

The actual year of my grandmother's birth will always remain a Classified Family Secret, but my best guess is that she and I were not born in the same century. Edith Navarre was one of five girls to be raised on a farm in Vienna, a French settlement on the banks of Lake Erie in Monroe County. Their only mode of transportation was a horse named Old Nell. The girls would huddle under a buffalo robe in the sleigh, as they sang, "Tramp Tramp Tramp, the Boys are Marching" on their way to the Little

Red Schoolhouse. It was all straight out of the *Little House on the Prairie* books!

There were stories of her grandparents, Mimi and Pippi LaPointe, who were raised in log cabins as children, and used sign language to barter money for muskrat furs with the Indians. My great-grandparents knew of runaway slaves who would make their way to an underground tunnel at the Ohio River in order to seek refuge Up North. My grandmother had once confided to me that If they were caught during this escape, the slaves were often put to death. I considered that Mr. Martin Luther King was right to put his Life On The Line for all the brutality his People had endured, even though from the looks of things around our town——he still had a lot of work to do.

After high school, Gra, at the advice of her worldly sister Dorothy, went on to attend Michigan State Normal College in Ypsilanti. As one of the few female college graduates in the early part of the twentieth century, Gra was Light Years ahead of her time.

I loved to delve through the old yellowed clippings from her years as a Girls Basketball Coach—a career that was subtly suggested to my grandmother with the assurance that it would not interfere with her regular teaching duties. Even though the decision was meant to ease the mounting Women's Lib pressures of the day, I'm sure that school administrator had no idea what he was up against with the determined Gra.

As it turned out, the team won the championship that year, and my favorite photograph was of these girls wearing funny-looking bloomers, locked in victorious hugs. A pretty twenty-something face with light brown hair and a beautiful smile represented my grandmother. The photo offered solid proof that she was indeed a young lady at one time—a fact I often found difficult to fathom.

But the high point of this old battered photo album was a

frayed newspaper article that dated back to President Roosevelt's term in office. As it was explained by Gra, she had been very active in something called the Democratic Assembly, where she worked closely with Dorothy McAllister, the National Chairman Of The Party. I thought this Dorothy lady was awful lucky to have been invited to be a Chairman for parties all over the world.

Anyway, as State Chairman for the Democratic Digest, Gra had broken all the records for the most subscribers ever enrolled in a Michigan precinct. (A fact that would have made Joe, Green With Envy, since he couldn't even get enough newspaper subscribers to fill our small neighborhood.) As it was, Eleanor Roosevelt, our country's First Lady, frequently attended the functions that were run by this organization, and was impressed with the strong results that were being achieved by my energetic grandmother. And that was how Gra had the amazing fortune to receive a personal invitation to a luncheon in Washington given by Eleanor Roosevelt herself!

I loved to pester her about the details of the event. "Gra, Please, tell me again what the White House was like!" And somehow, there would be unveiled another fine point that may have been overlooked in prior reports of the occasion.

My grandmother wore a dress that consisted of the finest teal-blue silk, trimmed in velvet the color of fuchsia. The crabmeat appetizer was served by Mrs. Roosevelt herself—a recipe that Gra absentmindedly stuffed amidst other family cooking secrets and simply entitled, *ELEANOR'S CREAMED CRABMEAT IN PATTY SHELLS*—and a pretty blue *Lenox* china dish was presented to all of the guests as a souvenir.

Before God finalized his decision to allow us children to enter the world, there was a short engagement to a fellow from West Point Academy. His name was Jack Leonard, and the ring that Gra would later return consisted of an exquisite diamond set in a beautiful mounting with the insignia of West Point. My grandmother was invited to attend all the graduation functions that year, and was easily the Belle of the Ball in her beautiful white taffeta dress trimmed with pink chiffon rosettes.

At the Graduation Ball, Gra actually danced with Dwight D. Eisenhower, a friend and fellow graduate of Jack Leonard's. First-run shows in New York City and many other West Point functions were all a part of this thrilling whirlwind courtship.

Alas, while poor Jack was away in Mexico on military duty, Gra fell in love with another young man named Hugh Navarre. According to her, it was better to select a man with a less prestigious title than one who was dictatorial and conceited—a fact I mentally filed away for future reference.

Gra and Hugh were married at St Joseph's church, and honeymooned at *The Island House* on Mackinac Island. With the usual efficiency of a good Catholic woman's fertility, Gra would soon bear her new husband three vivacious children, the youngest of which would be considered a Child Prodigy for her unusual intelligence—my mother, Carolyn. Together with her sister Mary Jane and brother George, they grew up in a household that emphasized higher education, strict morals, and a proud French heritage.

Later, it was said that my grandmother hovered more closely over the imaginative Carolyn, perhaps in an effort to quell the instinctive knowledge that told of my mother's eventual sway to the Beat Of A Different Drummer.

For now, Gra's strong points were definitely in the kitchen, where she churned out fresh roasted chicken, fluffy whipped potatoes, and mouth-watering strawberry shortcake. Since the small

Catholic family of three had miraculously multiplied into twenty-seven grandchildren, there was no shortage of an appreciative audience for her Sunday afternoon dinners. Gra's table was always meticulously set with silver and china, while fresh-cut flowers and whimsical centerpieces served as vibrant finishing touches.

There was a comforting aura presiding over my grandmother's home that hinted of grandeur and the innocence of days gone by. I soaked up this loving environment with the alert wariness of a baby robin about to be pushed from the nest.

6

October 1965

The smoldering tip of my mother's cigarette paraded across the rear view mirror just when the car lurched precariously near a cute little white picket fence. I wistfully imagined myself in front of a roaring fireplace in the living room of the charming little cottage, while Normal People brought me thick bowls of stew and hot French bread, all the while clucking that it was a miracle my True Identity had been discovered after all these years. "SUCCESSFUL RESCUE," *The Lansing State Journal's* headlines would blare, "A brutal Kidnapping that one sweet little girl had endured for more than eight years, has finally been discovered, as Annie Peters returns to her Real Family."

Everyone at school would gather around me in sympathy and I would be invited to all the right slumber parties. "There was always *something* about Annie that was different from those other Peters Children," Candy O'Brien would report to the school editor.

"The doctors have all said that driving is therapeutic," Gra announced, as if to reassure herself as well as us five children, who, as usual, were stuffed into the back seat of the newest vehicle. And then to my mother, "Maybe you *should* keep both hands on the wheel, dear."

Taking a deep breath, I settled back into the back seat, achingly aware that my mother, her dilated eyes appearing glazed and unfocused, held my whole life in her hands while induced with the latest Miracle Drug. I had to wonder if these doctors would so easily prescribe this treatment if *they* were part of this unsettling passenger experience.

Seemingly the only family member concerned with salvaging my life, I hunched over the front seat with alarm, only to inhale a large gust of secondary smoke. Settling back to my corner with a grumbling of annoyance, I wondered vaguely about the whereabouts of the last car and quickly surmised that along with the other procession of vehicles, it must have been quietly disposed of. My father was amused that Gra would merely call a local automobile dealer, and ask the Sales Manager to drop off a new vehicle. "Those Car Crooks," he chuckled, "are only too willing to saddle your grandmother with the Biggest Lemon on the Lot."

Meanwhile, Gra continued her endless quest to restore my mother's mind back to its original state which, my brother offered, must have been prior to meeting my father. Having found her own comforts through nature induced road trips, our grandmother was determined to single-handedly resolve both my mother's mental illness and our reckless childhood imaginations through roaming the countryside of Michigan. Hence, our relentlessly unpredictable Sunday Outings began. Everything from jaunts to a five-star restaurant that she had "just happened" to read about, to exploring the famous lighthouses of Michigan, was attempted with all the zeal of her pioneer ancestors. "Not even the most perilous adventures of these distant relatives," I acknowledged to myself, "could rival the harrowing experience of having my mother at the wheel."

On this particularly brilliant fall day, the essence of burning leaves exuded from an achingly crisp blue sky. Meanwhile, I was forced to endure the trampling of human bodies, while Gra gave in to repeated stops at red roadside barns for fresh caramel apples and hot apple cider. As the somewhat unclear destination of yet another distant Great Lake loomed ahead, I tried to suppress the churning inside my tummy, which seemed to escalate with each rustle of the burnished aspen trees.

We had each carved our own pumpkins that week, which would circle around the large Jack O' Lantern that my father took great pride in carving himself every year. Afterwards, Lisa had trouble lighting each of the five little pumpkins, as a great gust of wind began howling around our home. My father had finally managed to keep each of the pumpkins lit, but only after relocating the whole family of pumpkins to a spot more sheltered from the vicious wind.

Now, from my usual left-hand position in the back seat, I studied my mother's expression in the rear-view mirror. The latest drug experiments had graciously left traces of her original personality, which occasionally flickered back to life unexpectedly, reminding me of the weakening jack o' lantern which, at that very moment, was busy gasping for its life on the porch back at 721 W. Michigan Avenue.

Just then, the car began to jerk violently. As I checked to make sure the door was unlocked, just in case I needed to bail out, Lisa looked at me and began to laugh, which only added to my frustration. I shot my sister a dirty look and snuggled down deeper into my corner, contempt rising for the family that I had been stuck with.

Ultimately, encouraged by Gra, who believed in Music Therapy for just about any ailment including my mothers uncertain state of mind, the familiar song of our childhood began:

"I looked out the window and what did I see . . .
Popcorn poppin' on the Apricot tree!"

I had heard those lyrics a hundred times, yet at eight-years-old, they seemed to be making sense to me in a whole different way. We were singing a song that seemed to be perfectly describing what my mother must have been experiencing in her own fuzzy world. Angrily, I wondered why, in my short childhood experience, God had made me responsible for choosing the difference between Truth and Reality. I was just going to have to just flat out ask Him what He was thinking when he made the decision to replace our beautiful mother with this person who was becoming more and more like one of those empty pumpkin shells—with its own removable hat.

As the flickering light of the Jack O' Lantern died down to smoldering embers that Halloween, the final threads of reality seemed to tear from my mother's mind. The closet shelf that held her light-blue suitcases were gradually replaced by an empty space that quietly gathered dust, as we became frequent visitors to the Michigan State Mental Institution.

It was a crisp Sunday when my father led us past the barbed-wire fences that housed the area of the Mentally Ill. Massive turrets jutted into the Michigan blue sky like a castle in a fairy tale gone awry. It was said that as a former prison, the building had been considered unsuitable for criminals, and had since been approved as an institution for the growing number of patients who were not responding to the failing pharmaceutical experiments of the day.

After what seemed to be an endless series of gates and doors that required many chains, doorbells, and mysterious passwords, we were finally granted admission. Like the timid lion in my favorite movie, "The Wizard of Oz," I wanted to hear the words, "Go Home."

Shyly, we children nudged each other to be the first to brave this world of bright lights, harried nurses, and urine smells. I was confounded as to why these patients chose to Act Up in this manner; talking back, screaming at each other, and generally carrying on like that would get us marched straight to Sister Superior's office—No Questions Asked.

The Head Nurse locked us into The Dayroom, the final jangle of keys indicating that we were not to wander into any other section of the hospital. There was a tension in the air, as if the effort to conceal the usual activities of The Dayroom were just another added pressure on the staff. In what I thought was a pretty weak attempt to discourage any unwanted questions, the haggard looking nurses tried not to meet the eyes of us curious outsiders.

I tried to ignore one boisterous patient who was covered with peculiar bruises on his arms and legs, a side effect of the handling that seemed to be rougher than necessary. The smell of cigarettes, and the bars on the windows seemed to further confirm that this was not a short-term arrangement.

My mother was led into The Dayroom shortly afterward, wearing strange garments that were in sharp contrast to her usual stylish clothes. She seemed to be distracted as we children lined up to each bestow her with a tentative kiss on the cheek.

Reaching out to this new stranger seemed pointless since she didn't seem to care who we were, or the reason for our visit. In fact, her main focus of the day seemed to consist of completing the simple task of smoking a cigarette.

My mother's nurse, a tired-looking woman with an obvious mustache, delivered the most recent health report to my father with a phony attempt at kindness. "Carolyn's daily struggle to maintain any fragment of reality is noticeably weakening. However, there is a new drug called Lithium that is expected to offer a real breakthrough in the treatment of the mentally ill."

My guess was that from the look of things, this new Lithium had better be swift with its promise of an instant miracle. It was becoming pretty obvious that the People From The Other World were closing in fast.

We children counted the minutes until visiting time was over, and the Head Nurse wheeled my mother back to her private world with forced enthusiasm.

While driving home, I squeezed my father's strong right hand and gazed at the familiar profile of his handsome face. There were new lines around the soft brown eyes, but he looked around at our moping faces and quickly changed the mood. "Hey you kids, did I ever tell you about the time that the Cessna ran out of gas when we were up in Alaska's most dangerous territory?" Lisa chimed in with the details she remembered of the upcoming story and the atmosphere quickly gave in to the usual Peters cheerfulness.

While preparing dinner that evening, my father leaped from one sofa to another while accompanying Nat King Cole on an invisible trombone. We all laughed with sheer delight as he performed for our pleasure with puffed cheeks and wide eyes.

Father had the ability to make each day seem like a celebration. Since he relished being a child himself, the line between parent and child was often a very fine one. Easter Egg Hunts, individual boxes of chocolates at Valentine's, and creative birthday celebrations were all acknowledged with a joyful flair. Still, the leather bound camera was suddenly flashing at every turn as if he desperately needed to record our family unity.

After months of mysterious meetings, we children managed to piece together the fragments of information we were receiving through five empty water glasses that were pressed between our ears and the Piano Room wall—one of Joe's Science Experiments that didn't really work, although we generously gave him credit anyway.

We children had become Pawns (as my father angrily referred to it) in a long, drawn-out court battle that suggested "daddies" were not capable of being "fathers" on their own. All of his attempts to Obtain Custody as a Complete Parent were to "no avail," and finally, the quiet hushes that said we children would become official Wards of the Court.

This meant, said my father during what would be one of our last one-on-one chats for a while, that although I would continue my studies at St. Mary's Elementary, each afternoon I would ride with the others on the bus to St. Vincent's Home. The facility would serve as our temporary home until Other Arrangements Could Be Made. In the meantime, he would attend Mass with us at St. Vincent's each and every Sunday, after which we were allowed to spend the whole day together as a family. "But Dad, what about Christmas?" I exclaimed. "And worse, what about Felix?" I added, wondering about the fate of the tattered alley cat that had recently made a home at the foot of my bunk bed. Holidays would be shared in our home, my dad reassured me. And Felix our cat would be patiently waiting for our return. For a moment, I wondered what would happen if I just "forgot" to take that bus and walk to 721 Michigan Avenue after school, as usual. Instead, I decided to take the news like a Big Girl, knowing my father Had Enough On His Mind.

"Okay, Dad, we'll make the best of it," I promised, as he tucked me and Felix into bed with an extra hug. It was only after he Made His Rounds that I recognized a new stillness hanging over the household. Even Johnny Carson was absent that evening, exchanged for an angry silence hovering over my father's favorite Lay-Z-Boy chair.

The rhythm of the nun's mechanical pace at St. Mary's now seemed to pause when we children passed through the corridor to the Elementary School, their shadowed profiles searching our expressions for answers, and then just as quickly, casting down inquisitive eyes to clenched fists that held warm, familiar rosary beads. If I listened hard enough, I could almost hear their fervent mutterings become distinctly more pronounced.

As our Family Oldsmobile climbed up a long, sinuous drive-way, the words "ST. VINCENT'S HOME FOR CHILDREN" glared at me from a carved wooden sign. A dark blanket of clouds coincided perfectly with the cold autumn rain, as the largest Oak tree I had ever laid eyes on seemed to seek me out from the warm comforts of the back seat to offer a stiff wave of a gnarly branch. As we tentatively proceeded up the massive staircase toward an ornate doorway of the towering building, I knew that inside those walls, the discipline of St. Mary's would be mild compared to the military structure that awaited us.

"But why can't I just run the household, Dad?" Lisa was pleading just as the massive doors opened with a long creak.

Jean kicked Lisa in the shin, giving her a look that distinctly said, "Lay off—the decision has already been made."

The overseer of St. Vincent's Home, Mother Vivian, showed us into the sterile lobby with a warm, beaming face. "The Peters children! We've been expecting you!" she exclaimed. And then she added in a compassionate tone to my father, "There are a few more papers for you to sign."

As if materializing out of thin air, a nun with a brisk walk and a solemn expression named Sister Cleophas claimed us from the lobby to take us to our new quarters. Though her alarming overbite would put my newly protruding front teeth to shame, I noticed that she offered my father a coy smile.

My father embraced each one of us tightly, promising that he would be there to pick us up each and every Sunday. And as I reluctantly let go of his strong right hand in order to receive the cold, clammy palm of the beckoning nun, I realized with a sickening thud in my tummy that The People In The Other World had indeed won.

7

November 1965

The commanding orders of this Catholic Facility were The Daughters of Charity. In my opinion, the Daughters of Charity had it all over the Order of St. Joseph in the style department. Their elegant gowns seemed to float with a luminous shine down the long glossy hallways. Perched on their heads were lofty, stiff white caps that reminded me of two elegant swans in preparation for flight. Each outfit was rounded out by a large silver cross, which adorned the bandaged chests as if to contradict any suggestion of femininity.

We had already discovered that Sister Cleophas was not only cold and moody, but also had a complete distaste for anything that resembled affection. The title "Den Mother" must been bestowed upon her with only the scantiest consideration of its real meaning. We were cautioned by the other children that it was best to avoid her at all costs.

Approximately twenty-four girls and twenty boys lived at St. Vincent's Home for Children. Though the girls and boys had separate living quarters, we shared the dining room, chapel, and playground. As I forlornly watched my brother retreat to the other side of what seemed an ancient building of massive proportions, I was suddenly grateful for God's amazing forethought to space our births closely together just so Joe and I could still see each other every day in our classroom at St. Mary's Elementary.

The girls' sleeping quarters, which consisted of eight to a room, were broken down into three age categories: the Blue Room, the Pink Room, and the Sand Room. After much dialogue by the well meaning nuns—who were not, after all, prepared for such a large onslaught of girls—it was determined that the Peters Sisters were more apt to become better adjusted if we were all placed together in the Pink Room. And so, packing our items into the large shelves and closets that had been assigned to us, we gaily assumed the roles that we knew at home. Lisa instructed us to line up our shoes just so, and Jean had the forethought to create one extra closet for The Pile. This was a term that was used for clothing items we were willing to share with each other. A system that had always worked quite well for us as it meant Hands Off from favorite articles that you were not so willing to share.

As an extroverted and gregarious family, we spent most of the first day in front of one of the large bureau mirrors, singing and dancing one of the usual numbers that we performed for our parents. After all, Lisa had said that this short confinement must not interfere with the dreams we shared of being a version of the Lennon sisters.

Almost immediately, to preserve Peace of Mind in the Ward, it was determined that we should probably "interact" with the other children more, and so the staff reverted to a new strategy of securing us with more passive personalities.

My sister Theresa and I were assigned to the Sand Room with another pair of siblings known as the Ayala Sisters—two Latin siblings who didn't even go to Catholic schools. I just knew that Sister Josetta would have an Absolute Fit if she knew I was sharing my bed quarters with a couple of "Non-Catholics." After all, we had always been told by the nuns, in No Uncertain Terms, that it was considered by God to be a Mortal Sin to hang around with anyone that did not Share Our Faith, even if it wasn't their fault that they were not lucky enough to be born Catholic.

My bed was located in the left-hand corner of the room, its only distinguishing feature being the beloved stuffed rabbit sloppily perched on my pillow. "Harvey's" ragged pink nose and alert fuzzy ears seemed to survey the room with a cautious vigilance for anything that might invade my personal space.

Frances Ayala, who was two years older than me, knew without a doubt that there had been a serious mistake in her placement here, since she fancied herself to be Hollywood Material who somehow was mistakenly cast in this demeaning orphan role. In Frances's mind, this whole mix-up would soon be resolved, and there would be justice to pay for the poor souls who were responsible for this infringement on her career. In the meantime, she busied herself with learning the newest hairstyles and periodically assaulting us with hot rollers. Her own thick dark curls were often straightened by an old steam iron that was carefully hidden under her bed. I often marveled at her courage, because the mere contemplation of Sister Cleophas's reaction to this Sin was enough to Curl Your Hair forever.

Carmen was a younger, more practical version of her sister. She had a solemn, square face with thick dark hair that was straight as a board, defying the electric rollers and causing Frances much frustration.

The Ayala Sisters had the good fortune to be part of the Underground at St. Vincent's. This was largely due to their rough looking Latin brothers, Ted and Augustus, who resided on the Boys side of the facility. Setting their alarm for 3 AM, there would be a great scurrying of slippers and whispered hushes, as Frances and her sister Carmen would meet with a snow-masked member of this conspiracy at an undisclosed doorway.

After responding to muffled requests for all the proper identity: magazines, cigarettes, and Spearmint gum would be distributed in a plain brown bag. Finally, the quick tempo of padded slippers could be heard as the two sisters made a Big Show of sliding back into bed with their clandestine treasures while whooping with stifled glee.

Theresa and I tried to ignore the foreign language that the Ayala sisters shared like a secret code after Lights Out, even though we recognized some of the Spanish cuss words that would strictly meant as an attempt to get our attention. I had already explained to Theresa that we were Cut From A Different Cloth than that of our new Latin roommates, who were obviously straight from the streets of Detroit; and that therefore, it was best to remain silent. We also pretended not to notice the small flashlights that mysteriously appeared under their thin sand-colored covers, precisely at the same time as Lights Out.

"When is Dad going to come pick us up?" I heard Theresa's voice inquire one evening as the Ayalas' foreign tongue and culture was grating on my nerves.

I reacted to the question as any normal eight-year-old would when faced with being a sudden parent to a seven-year-old little sister. Playfully jumping into bed with her, I squeezed my little sister's small dimpled hands and twisted one of the platinum-blond locks that, together with her large blue eyes and porcelain skin, gave Theresa the perfect expression of a cherub doll. Now, pinning her arms down while pressing our foreheads together, I repeated the antic always guaranteed to make her laugh:

"Mick-ey Mick-ey Mick-ey Mick-ey Mo-ouse, Mick-ey Mick-ey Mick-ey Mick-ey MOUSE!!!"

After her laughter subsided, the inevitable, "Tell me a story" was whispered into the darkness. Snuggling deeper into Theresa's little arms, I began: "Once upon a time, there was a Rabbit named Harvey. Harvey wasn't just ANY rabbit . . ." and so began our favorite story of the rabbit that found a hole under a log in the middle of a deep green forest—only to fall into a new world where the animals talked, and the humans could only listen . . .

The next morning, the usual ear-piercing alarm snapped me to my knees with an abrupt force. Cradling my arms around my bowed head, I attempted to rise from the floor in a half-hearted attempt at morning worship. Grasping her rosary, Sister Cleophas commanded the Morning Prayer with a mechanical pace to each Ward. The icy-cold floors were a grim reminder of the early-morning hour, a fact that was now causing my knees to rebel as they attempted to adjust to this rude awakening.

Following Morning Prayer, all the children paraded downstairs, where we put on aprons and lined up in single file to enter the Dining Room for breakfast. Our aprons were clearly marked in black magic marker, a new policy that was suddenly branded on each of our personal clothes and toys. Theresa and I wore full aprons, while all the older girls slipped on half-aprons, as if in somber acknowledgement of the passing of their youth.

After breakfast, the ride to St. Mary's was undertaken with an enforced silence. Our school bus, which bore the words, "St. Vincent's Home for Children" in glaring black letters, was a true source of embarrassment to me. I saw the compassion in others' eyes that first day as "the orphans of St. Mary's" disembarked one by one.

My best friend, Mary Lou, viewed me in complete fascination for suddenly becoming "one of them," and pressed me constantly for information about the mysterious home that in her mind, held all the makings of Oliver Twist. Mary Lou had a mop of yellow hair and a spattering of freckles that did honor to her mischievous character. I did my best to tease her imagination with details of my new surroundings. With a silent acknowledgement of the monk-like existence and harsh treatment we were enduring, I spun a tale of betrayal that was exaggerated purely for my best friend's benefit.

Unfortunately, it wasn't long before my tales of woe seemed to take on a life of their own. Sister Cleophas felt that hard work and good convent living would keep us all out of mischief, and we were gradually cast into a formal regime that had all the trappings of a Catholic Boot Camp.

My efficient work habits must have become apparent to the germ-fearing nun, because within that first week, I acquired the elite new titles of Bathroom Scrubber and Dishwashing Trainer. In addition, I was required to polish 24 pairs of black patent-leather shoes with Vaseline until they gleamed. But the real reward would come later when, on that first Saturday morning, I was introduced to the "The Buffer." This was a monstrous, heavy-duty Floor Machine boasting a turbo-sized engine and self-propelled features that must have been way ahead of its time. I was very petite, and on more than one occasion I witnessed a Staff Nun, swiftly clearing the hallways in terror before realizing that The Buffer did indeed have a driver.

The sterile, gleaming floors acted as a bleak reminder of the lack of love and emotion that others must have experienced at St. Vincent's. I was supremely grateful that God had decided to shower me with siblings and a loving father who would be there for us at the end of each long week.

"DAAAADDDDDYYYYYYY!!!!!!!!"

Mother Vivian smiled as five children burst into the lobby to greet my father with unbridled enthusiasm. The unmistakable joy on his face was all we needed to know we had been sorely missed.

Bowled over by the rush of children, my father embraced each of us as he explained to Mother Vivian that this was the quietest week he had ever known. "TOO QUIET," he repeated—a subtle warning that the State had not heard the last of his repeated requests for custody.

In record time, we were out of the building and under the welcoming blue skies of freedom, the glorious day stretching ahead of us.

"Okay, one at a time," my father gruffly instructed with a smile that gave away his pleasure at the unceasing banter.

"Sister Cleophas hates me," Jean announced, which did not

come as a surprise to any of us. Jean, a raving beauty with jet-black hair, a heart-shaped face and vivid green eyes, had certainly been the scapegoat that week in more ways than one. Her looks were in such sharp contrast to the homeliness of Sister Cleophas that it was obvious to all there was another motive for the sharp insults that were hurled in her direction. Why, just that morning, Sister Cleophas had dished out another cold remark to Jean just a few minutes before batting her eyes at my father and fluffing her Nun Bangs.

After silently absorbing this fact, my father promised Jean he would have a talk with Sister Cleophas when we returned to St. Vincent's later that evening. We all rushed to Jean's defense, knowing that our father's solution would only wreak havoc on the situation.

"No, Dad, I'll deal with it," Jean offered, and my heart went out to this gallant sister whose future was certainly not looking very bright.

With her usual take-charge attitude, Lisa was usually in charge of the entertainment options, and could be trusted to wheedle my father into just the right adventures.

"Let's go to the Super Slide," Lisa suggested. We all ecstatically agreed, and for a moment, the fears of five confused children were forgotten as we headed to the Sears parking lot singing The Beatles brave new hit, "Lucy in the Sky with Diamonds." As my father sang along to the music that he normally teased us about, I settled back into the backseat knowing that my Life as I once knew it was now in the hands of the Catholic Church.

Our ballet instructor, Theda Assiff, was a petite Frenchwoman with three children who also resided at St. Vincents. The Demerit System of St. Vincent had already resulted in my missing both an

Art Class and a Ballet Class for Talking Back to Sister Cleophas, so I was determined to channel my energies in a more positive way. After all, less freedom and more restrictions quickly added up to lots of misery In My Book, as I mentally geared up for the overly programmed world of St Vincent's Home.

My sister Jean and I would practice on the empty stage every Saturday, since she had the enviable position of cleaning the auditorium. Escorting the brooms and mops that were our graceful dancing partners, we twirled and laughed with delight until inevitably, we would hear the sharp clicking sounds of Sister Cleophas's severe black shoes, and revert to a charade of furiously doing our chores. Her lips would purse as she would shoot us a look of disapproval that suggested there was no room for high-spirited girls in a Catholic environment.

One brisk November afternoon, after Study Hall, we were led out into the courtyard for scheduled Play Time, which that day, included a game of Kickball. Burnished orange leaves peered back enticingly from behind the black wrought iron gate that encircled St. Vincent's, as we were instructed not to go beyond the boundaries of the property. My heart sunk as I realized that even the best of my Escape Schemes would be impossible under the circumstances and I had better just Buck Up. I paused to wiggle my tongue into the empty gap that until just last night had held one of my front teeth.

Before the first jarring clang of the alarm could perform its rude awakening that morning, I had peered under the overly firm pillow of my bed, and frantically searched the floor, yet there were still not any visible signs of my beloved Tooth Fairy. Finally, I determined that the usual shiny dime had never been delivered, and that The Tooth Fairy was merely behind on her Route.

As I obediently took my place on third base, the white rubber ball was suddenly flying in my direction. Kicking for all it was worth, I found myself face to face with one of the burnished Aspen Trees that represented the forbidden boundary. At the same time, I noticed a car that was perched at a perfect vantage point to the playground. After only a brief hesitation, I realized that it was my father's car!

Quickly looking behind me, I jumped into the front seat with the same enthusiasm that had been perfected in our late-night clandestine meetings. My father smiled as he handed me a small white box. I quickly opened the lid to a shiny quarter that had been placed on a bed of cotton.

"The Tooth Fairy left that under your pillow," he announced in a gruff-but-kind tone.

Since there was no time for a hug, I jumped out of the car and blew him a kiss, winding my way around the corner with a calculated kicking that suggested a difficult maneuver had finally been accomplished. Careful not to drop the coveted box, I threw the ball into the hands of our unsuspecting playground supervisor, secure in the knowledge that The Tooth Fairies of America would always know exactly where to find me.

From where I slept, I happened to have a perfect view of the cemetery that resided in the next lot over—a daunting vision that seemed to leer at me as if to say that I was literally One Step Away From The Grave. The center of the cemetery boasted the huge old Oak Tree that had welcomed me upon my arrival. The towering tree possessed a thick hunchback trunk with massive arms and claw-like fingers. My guess was that purely for size alone, the ancient Oak must have been voted Administrator of the Cemetery years ago. I longed to hear the stories that it must have been bursting to tell.

The shadows of the tombstones took on an eerie glow that resembled Ebenezer Scrooge and the clanging spirits of *A Christmas Carol.* If I squeezed my eyes hard enough, I could sometimes see corpses of various shapes, sizes and ages opening their coffins and filing out to the tune of "Onward Christian Soldiers" or sometimes, the Beatles version of "Henry the Eighth."

The old steam furnace that made its home on the side of my bed seemed to offer a quiet companionship to my late night restlessness. I would count the seconds between the Gurgles, the Hisses, and finally the grand finale of the WHOOSHHHHH that preceded a hot blast of steam finally escaping from the confines of its metal prison—in perfect synchronization of my own buried emotions.

When my active imagination was not enough for the insecurities that threatened to bubble up from the surface like the hiss of the old steamer, I would often call on Christina. Christina was my very own star that would miraculously appear on command. She was much brighter than all the other stars—her radiance was that of the most brilliant diamond displayed on a bed of pure black velvet. With a glowing nod in response to my prayers, she would dart off into the night sky. Her lingering aura would silently acknowledge that my cause was indeed heard.

As morning would dawn on my small corner of the universe, I would often marvel at the light that receded from my window with an entirely different glow. The silhouette of the Great Oak seemed to surrender to the majesty of the sunrise—as the lumbering arms swept up with a graceful salutation to the day. Colorful cardinals would line up on the elegantly carved tombstones as they sang through the early mist with wild abandon—like unabashed suitors vying for attention. And then, the faint whisper of a distant promise would whistle through the wind of the mystical cemetery as if in answer to my troubled soul—"All Is Well."

8

December 1965

In a statewide attempt to free up the crowded Mental Institutions, my mother was temporarily released to my grandmother. Gra took this opportunity to take a voyage through Europe with my mother—perhaps in hopes that *International* Travel might be the cure for her mysterious mental illness.

Between excursions, my mother would make occasional visits to our new Home—accompanied by Gra, who in her current state of Denial, began to view St. Vincent's as a fine Catholic Academy. Their visits were always confined to the lobby, as if the dark hallway represented mysterious secrets that were better off concealed. As we wearily opened up the brightly colored packages and postcards of their travels to Switzerland and France, I couldn't help wondering how the Visitation Arrangements between my mother and us children had suddenly become reversed.

My mother now possessed a new drug-induced form of body language that seemed mechanical and dazed. It was as if the mundane physical travel of her body was in direct competition with the more colorful mental voyage of her mind.

As we watched Gra pack up the ribbons, paper, and exotic postcards, as if we were merely an errand on the way to their next destination, I met her eyes with my own questioning gaze.

"Okay, Carolyn, we have to go," Gra remarked with a new sense of urgency, avoiding my inquiring eyes. "Children, say goodbye to your mother."

We each lined up in single file to give our respects, humbly pecking my mother's cheek. I noticed that her right foot swung in tiny little circles with an uncontrollable new motion that began to irritate me. Why couldn't she just tell her foot to stop?

As I desperately searched her irises with a fleeting hope of recovering my mother's Lost Soul, I detected an unmistakable spark of love still exuding through the misty veil of delusion, like a faded tribute to the mother we once knew. But it was obvious that the beautiful blue green eyes were quickly changing into a swirling, violent ocean that threatened to swallow my mother whole.

We children trailed back to our rooms lost in our own thoughts. It was Jean who finally spoke up with a truth that rang through the empty corridor, leaving a chill of finality in its wake, "Well, I'm glad they're having fun traipsing around the world while we're stuck with Cleophas."

And suddenly from the shadows of her doorway, the spectacles of Sister Cleophas glistened in the moonlight. "You better just be happy I am willing to put up with all of you, Missie," she hissed with a snap of her fingers.

I gave Jean a compassionate glance as I slinked out of Sister Cleophas's way into The Sand Room, and quietly surrendered to my new surroundings.

After months of frequent hospital admissions and discharges between her travels, it was clear to everyone that my mother's last efforts were being lost to a greater power of pharmaceutical warfare. She had finally been diagnosed with a long-term mental illness called Schizophrenia, and had to give up the overwhelming struggle to care for us. The unsettling future of her family did not seem to have any visible effect, as the once brilliant mind shut down with a proverbial clang. My mother submitted to the warm blanket of her new hospital surroundings like a baby takes to its bottle. There seemed to be only a hint of reluctance as she formally checked out from the cerebral requirements of this world.

Sometimes, I thought about when Jean and I used to play Dress Up in my mother's large closet. Italian-made shoes, long white gloves and exquisite handbags lined neatly on the shelves. There were bright-feathered hats that lived in large round boxes fringed with gold rope. The scent of Chanel No. 5 perfume still lingered on her fine silk dresses.

These symbols of youthful hope were now quickly becoming fragmented pieces of the past. My heart went out to the father who hadn't forgotten his vows and the unspoken yearning for his creative and vivacious wife, who could only look at him now with hollowed eyes of confusion.

Since there was no obvious Light At The End of The Tunnel, we children were determined to make the best of things. One consolation in our new circumstances was that our new Orphan status began to earn us unexpected social invitations that year. This meant that at various intervals of the school day, an announcement would blare from the P.A. System that the children of St. Vincent's would be excused from St. Mary's for an afternoon Christmas party.

Appearing humble during these welcome distractions was usually quite difficult when faced with the envious expressions of the other students. Mary Lou would often accuse me of being an Orphan Imposter, since it was widely known that the Peters children went home on the weekends. But, silently and without much ado, I would solemnly gather my books and together with my brother, solemnly leave the classroom for the afternoon of relentless Christmas gifts and parties.

On this particular school day, we were escorted to the nearby airport for an afternoon Christmas Party, where it was rumored that Santa would be making an appearance.

After graciously accepting a welcoming gift of a Transistor Radio, I encountered Jean and Joe, who were still in shock at what they had just witnessed: According to them, a large yellow bus was seen pulling up beside ours in the parking lot As If They Owned The Place. The words, *Michigan School for the Blind,* were painted on the side in the same bold black lettering as ours.

As we watched, the blind children bounded out in excited enthusiasm for the unexpected outing, their eyes rolling unattractively in their sockets, like this was their first invitation of the year. To Make Matters Worse, we were *all* receiving transistor radios. "As if the handicap of being blind was contagious," Joe remarked.

Immediately, the blind students started dancing to *The Monkees* with strange gyratic motions. "Blind is one thing," Jean remarked, deeply offended by these unexpected guests, "but you would think they would have a little rhythm. After all, *Stevie Wonder* went to that school."

I had thought it was bad enough that St. Vincent's had swung some kind of deal for us to occasionally use the indoor swimming pool at the Boys Detention Center, which was located on The Other Side Of The Tracks in a spooky, red-brick building with wire cages on the windows. There were never any boys around when we swam, and I often wondered where they hid them. After each swim, I would scrub my body fiercely, determined not to let any Bad Boy Cooties leave a trace on my skin.

"I guess someone wanted to take advantage of a Two for One charity donation," Joe explained. "It's a better tax break for the end of the year." My brother could always be counted on to share his financial wisdom with the rest of us. I knew in my heart however, that even though he was miles ahead of me in Math, I was the only one in the class left standing at the end of our weekly Spelling Bee. Why, just last Friday, I had broken practically broken the record at St. Mary's when I successfully strung together all the right letters to spell the word: I-n-d-e-p-e-n-d-e-n-t.

Some of the usual glory was lost however, when the alarm rang out to practice for the big Nuclear Attack that was one day going to burn us all alive. Without a word, we had to "Proceed Quietly!" down all the fire escape steps of St. Mary's to The Basement. This cob-webbed dungeon held long dark tunnels, adorned with signs of Black Triangles on a bright yellow background of letters that blared: FALLOUT SHELTER. There were also numerous pictures of little girls around my age, falling to their knees with the statement, "If you feel hot sparks of fire, Get Down!" Mary Lou and I had decided that this regimen was really a scare tactic invented by St. Mary's, in the hopes that by giving us "just a taste" of what Hell was going to be like, we might reconsider our Sinful Paths.

Joe had been having a difficult time adjusting to the Boys Side of the facility. He had even gone as far as to run away from St. Vincent's recently. Since this grand feat involved covering more than thirty miles of territory, I suspected with a burst of pride, that my courageous brother may have even hitchhiked in his quest to reach my surprised father, who welcomed him with open arms. Nonetheless, after consuming a chocolate milkshake and a good night's sleep, my brother—who along with the rest of us was under something called Temporary Guardianship of The State—had to turn himself back in.

It seemed unfair to me that Joe's short career as a Fugitive was over before it had hardly begun. My father was making it up to him on Sundays, however, when the two men watched sports and took long walks after dinner. Joe was also given special privileges such as entire fishing weekends off as an extra reward for his bravery. Meanwhile, we women were usually saddled with the dishes and household chores. Although as self-proclaimed Tomboy of the Family, I was sometimes invited to the Tiger baseball outings with Joe and my father. I was very careful not to discuss the details of these events with my sisters, preferring instead to Keep My Lips Sealed. Eating my foot-long hot dog with a feigned interest in the game, I would become enthusiastic at all the right times. After all, you had to respect the privacy of the male clan if you wanted to be One Of The Boys.

As the Christmas party got underway, I was assigned to yet another Michigan State University couple who were my designated "parents" for the day. She was wearing a smart little navy suit, while he sported a v-neck sweater and dark crew cut. They both had matching chiseled smiles and dimples, and together, bore a striking resemblance to *Ken* and *Barbie*. We all went out to watch Santa arrive in the Parking Lot, as it was promised with all the usual gaiety, that this time, Santa would arrive by *helicopter* to deliver our gifts.

Huddled in the arms of *Ken*, I tried to take in the sights of the

Christmas celebration with all the delight I could possibly muster. Looking up into the cold blue sky, snow crystals were just beginning to form as we stood in anticipation for the helicopter that would magically deliver Santa. Widening my big brown eyes with the gracious charm of a deprived child, I snuggled deeper into the tall student's arms while his sophisticated blonde girlfriend cooed over me in exaggerated preparation of motherhood. I generously allowed *Barbie* to adjust my skirt against the cold gust of the helicopter as it landed with the deafening sounds of the powerful engine. I knew I had this role DOWN as I silently anticipated which new toys would fill my newly bulging toy locker.

Lisa was milling through the crowd with her usual diplomacy, shaking hands and smiling sweetly in hopes of finding a new Big Brother and Sister. I knew she had her hopes pinned on finding an opportunity to spend time away from Cleophas and St. Vincent's any way she could. I also noticed Theresa in the arms of a couple who looked as if they would take her home that very day–given the opportunity. Theresa's cherubic blonde curly hair and optimistic smile had them spellbound as they catered to her every whim. I made a mental note to make sure Theresa was securely on that bus for the ride back to St. Vincent's.

Santa disembarked in his bright red suit with a pillow that seemed to be dropping from the gravity of the helicopter. I gave him a quick appraisal before deciding that yesterday's Santa was much more authentic.

As we were led to the warmth of a crackling large fireplace in the airport terminal, I chatted with childlike enthusiasm to my new parents about the physical brutality inflicted on us by the nuns of St. Vincent's. And even though I was grateful for the daily porridge, a little seasoning would certainly lighten our load.

The young couple's eyes moistened as they listened with the exact level of sympathy I was looking for. Maybe they would talk to

Mother Vivian about being my official Big Brother and Big Sister. I enthusiastically agreed and at the same time regretted the decision. I had perfected my role of "Little Orphan Annie" to such a fine art that the requests to take me out of the Home on Permission were becoming too numerous. Mother Vivian had just talked with me in private about this very subject. Being the sole attraction of a Family that would take me out to indulge my every whim had become like a game, and I was quietly exercising this newfound influence.

I went on to politely explain to the students that my father, who had been in hiding my entire life had just emerged, and may want to spend some much deserved time with me. With much relief, we were suddenly interrupted by the exuberant voice of our excited host as I looked up to hear my name being called.

Excusing myself to claim what would surely be another Chatty Cathy, I made my way up to Santa, closely scrutinizing the beard that was slowly tearing away from his lip. Bending down, he asked me if I knew that Santa had a special present this year for me. I shook my head and sweetly declared that I wasn't expecting anything from Christmas but the love of our dear baby Jesus.

Responding with a pretty decent Ho Ho Ho, Santa pointed to the towering package by the fireplace that had aroused the curiosity of all the children. Running over to rip open the red-and-gold paper, I uncovered a six-story Dollhouse, complete with accessories.

My heart leaped as I lovingly observed each tiny piece of furniture with a bedroom for each child. But the tiny white provincial canopy bed, complete with its own desk and lace-skirted vanity, seemed to taunt me, as if to say that this lifestyle did not belong to me. I held the tiny porcelain figures representing each member of the family and lingered on the chiseled figures of the mother and father that clearly resembled my new college friends.

Suddenly, I was torn between the desire of the Dollhouse that I always wanted, and the Real Home that seemed like an elusivdream. An overwhelming sadness washed over me as I politely thanked Santa for his special gift, silently wishing that he would take this plastic promise of Suburbia back up to the cold elusive sky that it had been hatched from.

Temporarily released for the Christmas holidays, my mother shared the holiday festivities with a new numbness of her surroundings. Nevertheless, Gra did her best to create the Norman Rockwell atmosphere that was always a welcome relief from the frigid temperatures of St. Vincent's which, I was finding, rarely had anything to do with the weather.

Unlike the festive decorations that my father took great pains to display during the holiday season, Gra's home was adorned with just a few candles. But the warm aroma of mincemeat pie, and the bulky, hand-knit stockings that hung above the fireplace mantle, offered a simple, old-fashioned elegance.

"Why, thank you, Gra!" I exclaimed with unbridled enthusiasm as I took in the sparkling keyboard of my new typewriter. Leave it to my grandmother to bestow me with a Christmas gift that would be in complete contrast to the dolls my friends would receive that year.

Gra seemed pleased with my appreciation of her untraditional gift. "I'm going to teach Annie how to write a business letter," she proudly remarked. I jumped on the familiar plump lap and gave her a warm hug, thrilled to be the youngest apprentice to represent this long line of liberal Navarre women.

At my father's home, the Christmas festivities that year were performed with the usual grandeur: A fresh-cut pine tree strung with popcorn, mingled with the warm bread smells of my father's chestnut dressing. In the crevices of the bay window, fallen snow-flakes shared their space with the scarlet wings of a daddy cardinal. The neighborhood lampposts were adorned in soft twinkling lights, as if to bathe the cheerful carolers in a warm, tawny glow.

On Christmas Eve, there was a sacred hush in the air as we each placed one favorite shoe on the front porch in anticipation of a visit from St. Nicholas. I was stringing popcorn and pondering the fact that my father and his trusty camera always seemed to be absent at this point, when there was the inevitable knock on the door. With the usual exclamations of delight, we went outside and retrieved the treasured coins from the corners of our shoes. Meanwhile, my father mysteriously appeared from the kitchen to share in our amazement at the swift generosity of this mystical old Saint.

That particular evening however, my father still had on the shiny black boots with telltale signs of snow crystals—a surprising oversight effectively exposing his role of Saint Nicholas. Jean solemnly pointed the boots out to me with an expression that sternly warned of the consequences should our little secret be exposed. Feeling superior with this private knowledge, I pretended not to notice and counted my thirty-five cents with all the enthusiasm of the previous years.

Lisa carried out the 3 AM wake up call with all the usual stealth of Christmas morning. Ten pajama-clad feet meandered down the staircase in cautious anticipation of encountering Santa himself, only to find my grinning father instead. There was an uncommonly large stack of brightly packaged gifts that spilled out from under the familiar ornaments and warm scent of pine. It was as if by observing these traditions to the letter, my father felt he could protect us from the brutal force of a predetermined fate.

Edith Navarre and her sisters

Hugh Navarre, Gra, and Family

Family Photos

Gra and her father, Edward Drouillard, on her Wedding Day

Gra and Hugh Navarre in the Horseless Carriage

Family Photos

The Alaskan Cabin - Anchorage, 1955

Lisa, Carolyn, Joe, Jean, Bill in Anchorage, AK - 1956

Faith and Joe - a budding friendship

Brighter Days in Azusa, California - 1959

Family Photos

The Author at Two - 1959

Christmas in California - 1960

Faith, Jean, Lisa, Theresa, Bill, Joe California, 1960

Family Photos

St. Mary's School Days

St. Vincent Home

Family Photos

Traverse City, Michigan 1999

Grand Haven Lighthouse, October, 2001

Lisa, Jean, Carolyn, Joe, Theresa, and Faith 1999

Grand Haven Reunion - October, 2001
Theresa, Faith, Joe, Jean, Lisa

Family Photos

January 1966

As the Great Oak hunched his ice crusted shoulders toward the earth in an effort to ward off the next unexpected frigid gale, life as I knew it seemed to take on a certain rhythmic lull. Between residing at St. Vincent's, studying at St. Mary's, spending Sundays with my father and occasionally visiting my mother at the State Mental Institution, our steps became mechanical and softer–if only for want of a more peaceful existence. We learned to step into the rituals of each environment with a sacred respect of the traditions they each commanded.

Although weary of the continuous rules, we learned to carve out our own unique molds while Playing It Safe with the system. Our friendships and sibling relationships became the glue that helped us withstand the authority figures who repeatedly tried and failed to subdue our resilient spirits.

The playroom at St. Vincent's was bustling with the usual activities of dominoes, cards, and Barbie dolls. Frances Ayala and I had perfected Barbie's Fantasy Life down to a fine art. In our minds she was the ultimate Diva, determined to have it all. Using our imaginations, we could catapult ourselves into her world at any given time. On this particular day, Frances was demonstrating with supreme authority how Ken could make love to Barbie. Grinding their bodies together on the cold surface of the folding table, she explained that a baby would arrive in approximately nine months.

I pondered this fact, never having the experience of a mother to inform me of the Birds and the Bees, and realized with a horrible certainty that my parents must have accomplished this bizarre act at least five times in order to have us children.

Forcing myself away from the increasingly disturbing vision of my parents acting totally naughty even though they were Catholic, I sensed a strange hush come over the playroom. Apparently, a New Girl had just arrived at St. Vincent's.

Although the home was a short-term facility, most of us ended up there on a long-term basis of anywhere from three months to three years. The Ayala and the Peters children had Seniority, and with that came a certain amount of respect from the other residents. As Senior Members, one of our self-appointed tasks was to weigh the popularity potential of each new orphan as they arrived on the scene.

Leatrice appeared to be around eleven-years-old, which meant she would be assigned to The Blue Room with my sisters. There was more at stake however; this little transition would mean an instant promotion for Francis into the Pink Room, and I was in jeopardy of losing my Personal Hair Stylist altogether.

This child was altogether different than your average child at St. Vincent's. She was black, and although we had been exposed to different ethnic groups from an early age and had been raised to respect every race by my parents, our curiosity was definitely aroused by the FIRST black girl *ever* to arrive at St. Vincent's Home.

Sister Cleophas introduced Leatrice Owens to all of us with a fainthearted attempt at hospitality. Leatrice, who shyly looked around in hopes of finding someone, anyone, with a similar color of skin, bowed her head and fidgeted in discomfort. Feeling sorry for her, I immediately decided to take her in as a member of the Peters Clan.

The following morning, I witnessed two nuns in The Infirmary debating exactly what to do with Leatrice's hair. As my new friend agonized over their solutions for straightening, braiding, or applying chemicals, the verdict came back. It would simply be impossible to create Leatrice into a white girl; therefore, she would wear a wig. Thus, Leatrice donned a bad wig that she would forever despise. She did however, manage to keep a large pink comb stuck on the side of the wig—a trendy new look among the black people on television. I noticed that Sister Cleophas, in a rare display of kindness, did her best to Look The Other Way.

It wasn't long before we realized that Leatrice was a force to be reckoned with. The shy, reserved girl who we met that day in the Playroom quickly became comfortable with her new environment, and was determined to put some life into our dreary days.

Long-legged with beautiful skin and a wide, contagious grin, she bounded through the facility, dodging Sister Cleophas with quick finesse and creative excuses while playfully encouraging all of us to Break The Mold.

On one occasion, we watched in awe as Leatrice hurled herself down three flights of stairs, exclaiming, "Ooooooh, Cleophas is on the Warpath!" Running to catch up with her that day, Sister Cleophas must have wondered what form of delicate punishment she could come up with, since Leatrice's charm always outweighed her mischief.

Leatrice could outrun any of the boys, and we cheered in delight as she scampered around the softball field with the speed of a graceful panther, uniform skirts flying, skidding into yet another home run. Sometimes on these occasions, the hated wig would shift to the side, or even fly off, to the horror of all the spectators.

These awkward scenes were always met with solemnity from The Boys Team. Raul Lopez was still bearing scars from a brutal beating for his cruel remarks about Leatrice's matted hair. The details of this legendary game were still replayed in hushed whispers at each new orphan's orientation.

In no time flat, twenty-four admiring white girls were soon strutting down the hallways imitating Leatrice with sounds of, "Hmmmmmm, Chiiiiild! Who you lookin' at?" and other culturally exotic expressions.

The St. Vincent's Home For Children bus was now the scene of much curiosity when we pulled up to the entrance of St. Mary's school every day. With our newly adopted black attitudes, we would belt out hits from Diana Ross and the Supremes amid peals of laughter as we swaggered and pimped down the bus steps in our blue plaid uniforms.

Some of the girls of St. Mary's, taking their cue from the St. Vincent's girls, were even rolling up their waistbands two, and sometimes even three times. This was indeed risky, should the students get caught during Random Inspection of uniform lengths. This meant that when you were walking down the hall Minding Your Own Business, any of the St. Mary's nuns could order you to kneel on command. If your skirt hem did not touch the floor, you had to roll it down to the proper length in full view of all your peers.

"Chiile! Look at that . . . they *finally* figurin' out what it means to be Cool!" Leatrice announced, obviously pleased with herself for Stirring Things Up.

Mary Lou cheered us on with utter delight. She herself had been secretly yearning for her parents to finalize their divorce so that she could be granted admission to St. Vincent's, where (in her mind), she could get in on all the fun. And although Candy O'Brien, the Runner Up for Class President, did her best to appear disinterested, I noticed her blond page cut was unconsciously swinging to the contagious beat of the new Motown Tunes.

Ushering us down the bus steps and avoiding the usual greetings of the St. Mary's nuns, Sister Cleophas took all of this in with "Where Did I Lose Control?" written across her face. It was during these moments that Leatrice would stand behind her, teeth jutted out in a buck-tooth portrayal of Sister Cleophas, and imitate her while we all tried to keep a straight face.

It was a defining moment in my life to realize that one person *could* make an impact on an established environment. Only God could have provided such a perfect solution to our dilemma. By delivering the gift of a feisty little black girl from Detroit to Upset the System, He proved He cared. This reassuring thought would continue to sustain me in more unsettling days to come.

I made my way to The Blue Room, breathless with the recent news that I had to share with Jean: I had just been given the leading role of Sugar Plum Fairy in St. Vincent's annual ballet recital! As I skid past Buttons, the wiry Scottish Terrier that always accompanied Sister Cleophas, the tired old dog gave me an irritated look that suggested I was invading her territory. *Cute dog, but definitely adopting too many of its master's arrogant ways*, I thought to myself.

My navy-blue socks slid into The Blue Room just in time to see the gangly legs of Leatrice sprawled on the blue chenille bedspread, her body writhing to the Motown tunes spilling out of the transistor radio she held up to her ear. Offering one of her famous wide smiles with a flash of pearly-white teeth, she motioned for me to sit down at the end of the bed.

"Where's Jean?" I inquired, too impatient to accept the invitation.

"Giiiiiirl, your sistah was up *all* night. Hackin,' sneezin, coughin,' I thought I would *never* get any sleep. She had to go to The Infirmary," Leatrice added smugly, as if relieved to have a break in the usual routine.

"NO!" I exclaimed in horror.

The Infirmary was managed by a Want-To-Be Nurse named Sister Alfreda. Like all the nuns with formal professions, I often wondered where they had the time to receive appropriate training in their fields. What with Prayer, Meditation, and the occasional course in the Basics of Terrorism, it was difficult to imagine where the College Training might fit in.

Sister Alfreda had the body and jowls of a bulldog. Her neck was so massive that if our fevers ever spiked high enough, the large cross squeezing the center of her throat could sometimes take on the illusion of a studded collar.

The Infirmary was located in a lonely corner of the first floor, far off from any perceived civilization. Its small, sterile confines held a stiff narrow cot, a sturdy side table, and a plastic pitcher of water. Sister Alfreda, in her crisp white nurse's uniform that doubled as a habit, would perform her duties with a pinched expression that suggested you were One Step Away From Purgatory. Her pale-blue runny eyes would narrow in distaste and the fat around her pasty arm would jiggle just like banana pudding as she would pop a thermometer down your throat so deep that gagging to death became more of a distinct threat than a simple flu.

I once had the unfortunate experience of sliding down a tree and tearing a large gaping hole in my knee. I knew without a doubt that this tragedy had occurred out of sheer disobedience for being a Tomboy. Oozing with blood and guilt for my sins, I hobbled into The Infirmary, where I was made to stand in a corner and endure the agony of Sister Alfreda pouring Iodine directly into my open cut. Afterwards, I had to clean up the pools of my own blood from the sterile floor with a bucket of water that reeked of antiseptic. It was my first real moment of compassion for the way Jesus was humiliated during the Crucifixion, and I made Him a promise Right Then And There to start looking at Easter in a whole different way.

"Rinse the floor twice, and don't shove the dirt in the corner!" Sister Alfreda called out from the safe distance of the doorway.

"Easy Fido. Just because *you're* too fat to turn around in this dungeon . . ." I dared to reply Under My Breath.

Yes, getting sick was not what you wanted to do at St. Vincent's. It was much better to keep quiet until The Whole Thing Blew Over.

"Your sistah," Leatrice went on, "was hollerin' that she felt just fine the whole time she was pukin' on Cleophas. Lord, that girl put up a struggle!" She smacked her knee and laughed loudly, totally amused with herself.

Exasperated with Leatrice, I headed out of The Blue Room, smothering the urge to give Buttons a quick kick just for the unruly smirk on his face.

Rounding the corner to the infirmary, I stopped to find a large white sign posted to the window. "UNDER QUARANTINE," it said in big black letters.

I knocked on the window and Jean's pale, white face peered out with a bewildered look of surrender.

"Are you okay?" I mouthed.

As Jean nodded feebly, I noticed some peculiar new objects in the room. Beautiful flowers had been arranged by the bedside with a fluffy new comforter. The pitcher of water had been miraculously transformed into a delicate vase of the finest china, a small, rose-colored glass waiting beside it.

Hearing the brisk footsteps of Sister Cleophas, I decided to hide under the staircase. This time however, there were other, heavier steps sounding above me. Sister Cleophas was in one of her flirtatious moods, giggling happily beside a young, handsome man who was carrying a black satchel.

"So nice of you to call on our lovely young patient," she preened.

I couldn't believe my eyes: It was an Outsider! My sister was so ill that they had to call in a Real Doctor! I huddled in the corner, straining to hear more.

"So how are you, young lady?" the doctor asked as he looked around. "Nice room," he added.

Jean nodded and mumbled a response to his greeting that was too muffled for me to hear.

"Oh," said Cleophas with a unrecognizable lilt to her voice, "we try to make our Infirmary as bright and cheery as we can under the circumstances."

I risked a peek around the corner to get a better look at the situation. Jean had been propped up with four fat pillows instead of the usual flat one, while the doctor peered down her throat. I cringed in perfect tandem with my sister as I saw the large needle pop out of the bag and make its way into her arm.

"That should do it," the doctor said with a pat on her head. "You'll be on your way in no time!"

"Thank you, Doctor; and again, your generous contribution to St. Vincent's will be remembered!" Sister Cleophas gushed as she ushered him through the door.

I stayed crouched in the same position for a few moments, not daring to make my presence known, when suddenly the footsteps tapped back into our direction at a much quicker pace. It was Sister Cleophas, quickly making her way back into The Infirmary while pushing a metal cart on wheels. "You won't need *these* any more," she announced matter-of-factly. "The doctor says you're fine."

With that, the beautiful flowers and porcelain pitcher were whisked up and placed on the cart. The fluffy white comforter was traded in for one of our usual thin cotton blankets. Finally Sister Cleophas whirled down the hallway, wheeling the cart of luxurious goods back to the nuns' quarters, where they had come from.

I shook my head and wandered back upstairs, stopping to kneel before the statue of Jesus of The Sacred Heart. The wounded heart was bleeding, and his tender expression suggested that poor Jesus really was carrying the weight of the world. I was starting to know how the guy felt. Why, just yesterday, I had been paddled by Cleophas just for crawling under one of the library tables while searching for a pencil that I had dropped during Study Hour.

"Lord Jesus," I implored with all the earnestness I could muster, "thank you for making my sister all better. And I am sorry that I pulled the eyes out of Theresa's stuffed Easter Bunny, just because I liked her yellow bunny better than the brown one I got. But please, if you are indeed our Savior, find a way to reveal the real truth of Sister Cleophas." And as I rose, His eyes seemed to well up with compassion as if to say, "I heard."

The following week, I performed a meticulous rendering of The Sugar Plum Fairy. Everyone attended, including the nuns of Saint Mary's and my father, who happened to be Bursting With Pride.

After the show, while everyone was busy with tea and cookies, some nice ladies who said they were with The State took my hand and asked if they could look at the rest of the facility. I chatted on merrily as I gave the ladies a tour of our rooms, even though in our haste to get ready for the performance, we had all been given a rare opportunity to not have to make our beds that day.

When the nice ladies began to ask lots of questions, I only hesitated for a brief moment before deciding that The Whole Truth and Nothing But The Truth was the way Jesus of The Sacred Heart would want it.

10

May 1966

Lolly Bellgowan brushed past us with a smirk as she was excused from the meeting that had been called by Sister Cleophas that day. We were once again the victims of a new hormonal wave as the tired nun rallied on in an unending pursuit of the Virtues of Cleanliness. Lolly, with her blushing pink cheeks and freshly washed hair, was excused from the meeting since she obviously knew what it was to be a Real Lady. As for the rest of us, it was apparent we were not familiar with the term.

Meanwhile, Jean was still fuming with the fact that Cleophas, of all people, had been the one to explain the reason for her monthly period. This important milestone had coincided perfectly with Leatrice's first brush with *her* Little Visitor: An occasion that inspired Sister Cleophas to make a rare appearance into the Blue Room with little cotton diapers and a film that was played on the wall using a "new fangled" projector, a product of the recent State budget money. Even more embarrassing was the fact that Ted Ayala from The Boys Side was instructed to set up the confusing device. Ted had taken great pains to prolong his visit by tinkering with the machine for hours while Taking Shots at all of us girls as we innocently walked to the showers in our bathrobes, only to scream upon noticing that there was a forbidden boy in the dorm. Leatrice explained that this was simply an opportunity to horrify us with the morbid details of the plague that would haunt us for the rest of our life, all because of boys like Ted who would try to put his Thing in you if he ever caught you naked.

"Cleophas," she had howled, waving a Kotex in the air, "had us all in stitches, but we knew better than to be laughin' at her, since she was all tongue-tied about makin' love."

As Sister Cleophas continued with the lecture, I noticed that she seemed more haggard than usual. My heart went out to her for just a moment, as I considered that this group may have finally done her in. Right around midnight the week before, three of the girls in the Pink Room had been found missing. It was later discovered that the boys had dragged them out of their beds, and after raiding the refrigerator, had asked the girls to Take Off Their Tops. Frances Ayala, who had willingly obliged, was whisked away for an hour every day after that to have long, drawn-out counseling sessions, plus many Acts of Contrition—the most shameful of which was her demotion from the Pink Room to The Sand Room, to wallow in her sins for the rest of her days. As the youngest girls of St. Vincent's, it was no secret that the Sand Room represented the lowest members of the proverbial food chain. This particular penalty must have struck quite a blow to the fragile ego of Frances.

"Why, only yesterday, I couldn't help but notice that a couple of you girls were playing on the swings with the sole intention of letting the boys look at your underwear," Sister Cleophas persisted.

I could not refrain from asking the obvious question that seemed to be hanging in the air. "Excuse me, Sister Cleophas," I ventured.

"Yes?" she responded with an expression that suggested she wasn't really sure which Peter's girl I was.

"I was just wondering why we couldn't wear shorts or pants for our play clothes."

As everyone gasped at my unexpected courage, Sister Cleophas' steely blue eyes bore through me as if she suddenly remembered that I was the one responsible for the Bathroom Episode that had recently earned me five whole demerits.

At the time, I thought that I had calculated my plan pretty carefully. First, I had filled one of the bathtubs with warm water and lots of bubbles. Then climbing up the wall from the shower that separated the tub, I prepared to hurdle the eight-foot wall into the warm water below. Unfortunately, just as my naked body was crouched on the top of the wall, Sister Cleophas happened by with her arms full of fresh white towels. Our eyes locked in the mirror below at exactly the same moment as her face became contorted with the absolute horror of this situation.

Snapping her fingers at me in the mirror, she simply stated: "I will talk with you later."

I slowly slid down the knobs of the shower wall and watched my skin wrinkle into a raisin-like texture as I contemplated jumping out the window to escape to my father's house. Watching the steam evaporate into the sterile white walls, I whispered that if I had only one chance for my Guardian Angel to rescue me from danger, I would be willing to forego all future protection rights for the opportunity to keep my life. Finally, I went to Seek My Sentence in what would surely be the most record-breaking punishment St. Vincent's had ever known.

Walking quietly into the Den, I almost stopped in my tracks when I heard the sounds of tinkling laughter. My sister Lisa was telling a funny story that had found its way into the deep confines of a personality that Sister Cleophas might have once possessed, before the cobwebs set in.

I stood there transfixed as the nun wiped tears from her eyes, while accelerating the usual rocking motion of her chair. Shooting Lisa a look of ultimate gratitude, I timidly asked Sister Cleophas if she still wanted to have that talk. To my utter astonishment, she hiccupped a little and suggested that I not take up all of the water supply next time, and that a penalty of five demerits would be sufficient as my punishment. Even though five demerits meant forfeiting all desserts and extracurricular activities for one month, along with additional toilet duty, the thought of not being banned to Hell by Sister Cleophas for prancing around naked, seemed an overwhelming relief just the same. It was clear that my Guardian Angel had not Dropped The Ball after all.

Now, knowing that I had still had sufficient grace left over from my Guardian Angel experience, I had decided to get a little more mileage out of the situation. There was a silent pause as all ears awaited the results of a conversation that could make or break our ever-decreasing popularity in the Sixties Fashion World.

"Everyone knows young ladies would never be caught wearing pants," Sister Cleophas responded with an air of someone of high-class breeding.

"But Jo in *Little Women* sometimes wore pants," I argued.

She contemplated this, and for a moment, I thought there would be some relief to our mundane wardrobes that were carefully calculated into three distinct groups of Church Dresses, School Dresses, and Play Dresses.

Leatrice, who in that very moment had some bright orange madras shorts smuggled in her underwear drawer, gave me a smile like that of a professor satisfied with the progress of her student.

However, our hopes were quickly dashed as Sister Cleophas shook her head and looked down at the curling black toes of her shoe with a wistful look of discouragement. After the predictable long pause, she released an exaggerated sigh that indicated, through no fault of hers, that we were indeed Destined For Failure in this world.

Bowing our heads in feigned disgrace, Leatrice and I stole a look at each other as if we knew what was coming. And, just as we suspected, Sister Cleophas chose the two forms of punishment that were guaranteed to make each girl squirm.

"All right, I want everyone to stand in a single file line over on the far wall. And there will be NO bathroom privileges during this time."

We all looked at each other in horror for the inevitable punishment that was about to unfold. "We will be cutting EVERYONE'S bangs," Sister announced with supreme satisfaction. With a military lift to her shoulders and a determined expression, she led her reluctant prisoners to the cutting stool in the corner.

Jean was the first to undergo the vicious snips of the scissors. As my sister turned around to allow me to step up to the gallows, I avoided her eyes as I saw the short uneven line of hair where there were once shiny black bangs that had been the envy of her classmates.

"Lolly will be supervising uniform lengths, so please follow her into the next room," was the next statement of betrayal by the merciless nun. Unrolling our skirts, we knelt on the floor in a single line, casting Lolly a mass look of attempted murder should she even think about reporting the true lengths we wore outside of St. Vincent's Home.

Later that evening we lolled on our beds in our pajamas, pressing pink hair tape and Dippity Doo on our bruised egos and hairstyles in an attempt to get them to stretch overnight.

"It was a good try," Theresa offered from the next bed over.

"Yeah, Annie; for a minute I thought it might happen, but you know Cleophas don't know NUTHIN 'bout bein' cool," Leatrice remarked from the hallway. "Never has . . . never will. That woman has a Streak O' Mean in her that's so far down it ain't *ever* gonna find its way back up."

With that, Leatrice—who had once again been excused from the Bang-Cutting Slaughter—shuffled off in her pink fuzzy slippers. Jean nudged me and we suppressed our laughter at the tiny piece of hair tape perched squarely on the carefully curled bangs of Leatrice's new Aretha Franklin wig—a small symbol of support for the injustice that had been endured that day by her white sisters.

Meanwhile, Frances wiped tears from her eyes as she surveyed the destruction of months of hard work. Sighing, I allowed her to walk up to me with her newest contraption called a Curling Iron, silently surrendering to the pain that according to Frances was the only road to beauty.

December 1967

"And don't forget to look both ways," Mother Vivian murmured with the detached tone that seemed to be an inherent quality of nuns.

I nodded and ventured across the street, securing my rabbit-fur coat and clasping the matching earmuffs against the blustery cold weather. The snowflakes were falling in a soft, graceful dance, defying the force of the demanding wind. The four quarters that had just been bestowed on me by the charitable nun were creating a pleasant crease in the palm of my hand, as I clutched them in my fist with a viselike grip.

It was determined that I would take the bus downtown to get my braces tightened. After that, I would go to the Eye Doctor's office, which was exactly five buildings down on the left, to pick up the new glasses that had been ordered for me. There would be no dawdling, and No Talking To Strangers.

I had convinced Mother Vivian that according to the St. Mary's Order of St. Joseph—who might get their information from a different source than the Daughters of Charity—that there had been a recent bus-fare increase, due to Cost of Living and all, and that I would probably be needing two more quarters. Now, as the bus screeched to an abrupt halt in response to my wire tug, I was relishing my new authority, pleased with my success at doubling my allotted income.

I raced up to the third floor of the Capitol Building just to confirm that the Portraits of the Presidents lining the rich, cherry-paneled walls were exactly as I had remembered them. Since our house on West Michigan Avenue was only five blocks away, my siblings and I used to terrorize the building on a regular basis. When they thought I was old enough to understand, Jean and Joe solemnly pointed out to me the bullet holes that distracted from the portraits. I was however, still grappling with my brother's explanation of the Shoot Out that occurred on one tragic day, causing the entire Assembly to take cover from the Michigan Madman named Otis, who still resided in the County Jail. Content to see the Capitol building exactly as we children had left it, I continued on my journey.

Shauncey was busy trimming a handlebar mustache as I tried to slip past our neighborhood barbershop unnoticed. He had been our family barber for years, and would definitely be expecting some answers to our sudden disappearance. Visiting Shauncey's Barber Shop was always a pleasant experience, since in stark contrast to Cleophas, my mother possessed extraordinarily good taste. "We would like a pageboy cut for Annie today," she would inform him as she smoothed my cowlick with the confidence of one who studied the latest fashion trends.

Just as I was dodging under the red and white pole of the shop, Shauncey and I made eye contact. Hastily excusing himself from waxing one side of the mustache, he opened the old oak medicine cabinet that held the candy usually reserved for a haircut and selected my favorite.

"Annie, my dear, how are you and how is your mother? It has been quite some time since I have seen Hide Nor Hair from any of you!"

I gave him the usual, "She's not feeling great these days," and quickly departed with a grateful nod for the Hershey's Kiss.

A few minutes later, I slipped into the Dentist Chair at Dr. Benson's office and patiently held my breath as his entire fist invaded my mouth. This time, I remembered what Lisa had told me and tried to breathe out of my nose so as not to gag. Afterwards, I accepted the little paper cup of peroxide while avoiding the stern, questioning little eyes of the dentist. Preparing my answer for the inevitable lecture, I spit into the swirls of the round white sink and cleared my throat. "St. Vincent's Home is on a budget," I informed him earnestly. "That means we have to cut down on toothpaste and dental floss."

To my surprise, the sermon was actually cut short as Dr. Benson gave me one last warning and the flash of perfect teeth that represented one of his rare smiles. The fact that the brutal procedure of tightening my braces was not causing the usual watering of my eyes, further confirmed that this time, the old wheezer had gone easy on me. Even so, I stopped next door at The Peanut Shop, lingering just for a moment on a savory lemon drop before settling on a chewy caramel that would surely horrify the unsuspecting dentist.

I stopped on a corner bench to carefully count the 23 cents that had been given to me by the red-haired sales clerk with bad acne who had made it clear I wasn't worth the two-cent transaction. Quietly chewing my caramel, I reflected on the terrible misfortune that awaited me at my next destination: It had been discovered that I needed glasses. All my attempts to conceal my squinting in order to see the Psalm Board at church were to no avail. Sister Cleophas, who had pounced on this new information with the appetite of a fashion-eating shark, had personally chosen the style of glasses that I would be wearing to my Social Death. "I selected just what all the college girls are wearing," she had informed me with a sinister smile.

Gathering my courage, I stepped into Wallace Opticians and surveyed each of the scrubbed young faces. As they in turn quickly scanned the doorway behind me, I sensed that they were expecting an adult to be hovering in the vicinity—a natural response to the way things worked in the real world.

I made my way to the "Cute Boy" who presided over one of the large oak cubicles. "My name is Annie Peters and I am here to pick up my new glasses," I announced, batting my large brown eyes at him as if this flirtatious gesture could change my despairing situation.

As the young optician rummaged through a file to find the hated spectacles, I held my breath. Nothing however, could have prepared me for the atrocity that revealed itself in the next moment: Pale-blue plastic frames, swooped into an exaggerated cat eye and rimmed with tiny pink gemstones, were gallantly propped on my nose. Once again, Sister Cleophas had managed to outdo herself in the Fashion Institute of Ugly. This grim fact would certainly be confirmed by Leatrice when she laid eyes on these beauties. I pictured her holding them up in the Dining Room that evening at dinner and then putting them on while stumbling around like Mister Magoo for everybody's amusement and my horror. No, the glasses would have to be hidden away until I could properly digest the crushing humiliation.

Sliding off the stool with all the urgency of one who is On A Tight Schedule, I jerked the glasses off my face.

"I want you to at least wear them out of here," said the Cute Boy.

Popping the atrocious spectacles back on under the watchful glances of the now-sniggering Opticians, I made my exit and then immediately took them off again. Cursing Sister Cleophas under my breath, I promised myself that she would pay that following Sunday, when my father learned of this humiliating incident. But then, just as quickly, I remembered the recent Sibling Pact to not communicate these things to my father, who already Had Enough On His Mind.

Later, slurping my vanilla malt from the frosted silver shaker at the Woolworth's, I marveled at how God had managed to know it would cost exactly forty-eight cents for me to engage in this experience. For every Sister Cleophas in the world, there was indeed justice in the end.

12

April 1968

The angel of mercy caught God's attention that spring. There were to be some Changes In Store, my father had accurately predicted, since "the operating procedures representing St. Vincent's Home were not 'compatible' with the new psychological methods of the day." Almost overnight, there was an attempt by the State to free us from the nuns. It was with vast relief that we suddenly found ourselves with less-stringent boundaries as the nuns of St. Vincent's seemed to silently retreat back into the familiar walls of the home.

The excited whispers of rumors were flying as we were intro-duced to a young man named Dave, who was to be our new Coun-selor. We shyly took in the faces of the boys that had always been kept at a safe distance as we considered the daring new changes ahead. Both sexes would now be merged under the guidance of this new college graduate. Handsome, strong and brimming with adventurous ideas, Dave whirled on to the scene with a surprising mix of lighthearted enthusiasm and mischief.

In addition, our new Counselor had a degree in the Performing Arts, and could easily switch to Basic Military Training strategies whenever a nun came around–which automatically endeared him to staff and children alike.

Suddenly, meals were served in a bustling new atmosphere that included not only Open Discussion, but fun and games as well. Dave would have the young pre-teens flirting and giggling with him as he walked around the tables, playfully squeezing the giant rollers that were the result of much primping. Even Leatrice was challenged by this new personality that could rival her own talent for drama and humor. Debbie Stauffer, a Blue Roomer who was chummy with my sister Lisa, was currently basking in her newfound role for having the Biggest Boobs. Here was a handsome guy who she could finally try out her New Feminine Moves with. Debbie batted her long eyelashes at Dave and tried desperately to gain his attention but to no avail. Dave understood his role very well, Thank You Very Much, and a progressive future with managing 45 captivated children was infinitely more inviting than marriage in his immediate future. "That girl thinks ole' Dave's gonna be her Meal Ticket out of here," Leatrice whispered to me after one par-ticularly embarrassing moment, when Kathy appeared for dinner with a coral blush that literally screamed Walgreen's Discount.

Formal dinners were an exciting part of the new agenda, with proper etiquette and elegant new foods being introduced all around. We had even been given the opportunity to participate in weekly Talent Shows after dinner. The concept of tapping into our own originality seemed a Far Cry from the familiar patterns of conformity that had been our way of life.

Meanwhile, I was basking in my recent promotion to The Pink Room, which had become a dorm room of sorts, with three other girls my age including Kathy Sutter - my newest Best Friend and constant companion. Kathy and I shared soccer, ballet, prayers, and camp together with a fervent zest to keep our independence. It also helped that we were the same size, and could produce outlandish new styles from our connecting wardrobes to create private little fashion shows that were strictly for the benefit of the Pink and Blue Rooms. Rhonda Crawford and Sophie Thom, our two other roommates, proved to be loyal followers and could be counted on for Set Design as well as Fellow Fashion Critics. Francis was occasionally admitted for Hair and Makeover sessions–but afterwards, it was almost sad to see her depart humbly back to her sleeping quarters in The Sand Room, while the youngest girls giggled unmercifully at her attempts to tease her thick black hair into the latest lofty beehive.

Right now, Kathy and I were Making Ourselves Busy pushing two dining room chairs together as we nervously gathered the props for our appearance. On this particular evening, the stakes were high for winning the best skit of the three that were to be the evening's Talent Show competition. The winning cast would be excused from Dishwashing Duty for one whole month! As the heavy colonial chairs scraped against the shiny floors with an irritating screech, I caught the disapproving eye of Sister Cleophas, and knew without asking that I had just been awarded the Dining Room for additional Buffer Duties.

Attempting not to let the incident affect my performance, I took my place behind Kathy's chair in our makeshift *Bicycle Built for Two*. All eyes were upon us as Kathy, clearly the one with the stronger theatrical abilities, announced our intention to sing.

We had put much thought into our costumes for this special number: pedal pushers, baseball caps, and matching white sneakers were the envy of the other teams who seemed to have forgotten that Wardrobe was the most important element of acting.

"Dai-sy, Dai-sy . . ." Kathy was already singing and I began to chime in. Suddenly, I looked up and saw Leatrice grab an impromptu prop that would be perfect for her role as George Harrison. I lost all concentration as she plopped a kitchen mop on the lopsided wig, and immediately looked my way, as if seeking approval. As I observed the solemn stares of all the children at St. Vincent's, a latch seemed to come lose somewhere within the deep box that I had buried within the rigid years of Catholic Institutions. Falling off my chair with glee, I laughed and laughed as layer upon layer of emotion seemed to take a final departure from my spirit. Leaving in its place, a newfound liberty that, I knew in that moment, no one could ever destroy.

Kathy quit pedaling to turn around and look at me in total disbelief for my immature response to this much-rehearsed production—which only resulted in a new round of mirth for me. Finally, she got off the bicycle in disgust and I mumbled an apology to our audience as the opposing team took their place on stage. Leatrice and her team of fellow Beatles confidently finished a perfect rendition of "Let it Be," and humbly accepted the coveted prize.

The next morning, I almost collided with Sister Cleophas as I was expertly rounding the corner with The Buffer. Standing to one side, I patiently waited for the inevitable reprimand that was sure to follow my "unwarranted behavior" that had occurred on the evening before. To my surprise, Sister Cleophas had been crying, a soft white tissue even now being pressed to the corners of her steely blue eyes. She held in her hands a pillow, a thin blanket, and a few other items that were the composite of her earthly belongings. Buttons stood staunchly by her, a slight growl escaping from his throat at my sudden appearance. I had already overheard the recent gossip that her supervisory duties were no longer needed by the new State Run Facility and she would be moving to another section of the home. As I prepared to slink by her in the hallway the familiar scent of Ivory soap and starch loomed between us, and I considered giving her frail shoulders a quick hug of reassurance. But the vulnerable moment was forgotten, as instead Sister Cleophas surveyed my right foot, and with pursed lips, declared that her one hope was that in the future, I might one day learn how to tie my shoes.

Nodding my head in exasperation, I inched my way past Sister Cleophas—with one last threatening look back at her ornery dog. Buttons was wearing an undeniable smirk on his face as he trotted smugly behind her. Rolling my eyes, I squatted down to tie my shoe and pull up my knee socks—just in time to hear a loud wail from The Blue Room. There I found Lisa and Leatrice hovering over the radio, their faces stricken with some unexpected news. "Not Bobby!" Lisa cried as the radio repeated the announcement that Robert Kennedy had just been shot. Leatrice, who was still reeling with the rest of the world from the death of Martin Luther King Jr., folded my sister into a solemn embrace. Two sixties teens of two different colors and backgrounds. Confusion reigning over the loss of our Leaders, the loss of our family structures, and the bittersweet anticipation of knowing that no one could take away our individual power, nor our ability to make a difference in the lives of those around us.

In the meantime, we children were still alternating Sundays

at my father's, with occasional weekends at Gra's whenever my mother was released to her care. Oftentimes, this meant engaging in "Indulgence Therapy," as my father wryly referred to it, which consisted of driving around the entire state of Michigan with my mother at the wheel, while Gra sought out new restaurants and activities that might stimulate her daughter's brain back to health.

With Gra, who had never owned a driver's license, instructing my mother from the passenger seat, we children would hold our breaths from one destination to the next. The thought occurred to me that we were, after all, living on borrowed time, and that our five Guardian Angels might just Trip Up one day and allow the car to career right into a tree.

One of the few traditions that could be counted on was the smoldering ash of my mother's cigarette. It didn't help that all the tobacco companies relayed continual messages of persuasion from our favorite rock and roll station, as well as from the cover of all the fashion magazines. "You too," the jingle hissed, "could be the recipient of both a Slimmer Figure as well as a chance to assist with the entire progress of The Woman's Liberation Movement. The only thing we ask is that you inhale toxic smoke from these little rolled numbers, directly into the cavity of your lungs."

The ridiculous length of the cigarette, now complete with a little plastic tip, would burn endlessly as I held my breath against the unwanted aroma. Since no one else seemed to notice that we might all just Go Up In Smoke, I would request on a regular basis with growing exasperation: "Mother! Will you please flick your cigarette?" all to no avail. The others, immersed in their own forms of escape, would only gaze at me with blank, hollow looks, as if I was disturbing their worlds by encouraging them to come back to reality. There was however, some consolation from the fact that the newest model Oldsmobile had leather seats along with a tidy little pocket to store my *Mademoiselle* magazine and chewing gum. Secretly, I reveled in the fact that One Day My Prince Would Come, and I would be able to finally get away from these people altogether. Until that day, I would just have to patiently bide my time. But just then, in an obvious gesture to dismantle my peace altogether, the jingle of the offending cigarette rang through the speakers of the radio behind my head:

YOU'VE COME A LONG WAY BABY!
TO GET WHERE YOU'VE GOT TO TODAY!
YOU'VE GOT YOUR OWN CIGARETTE NOW, BABY!
YOU'VE COME A LONG LONG WAY . . .

In my opinion, if this new Women's Liberation Movement had only accomplished getting us all a crummy little cigarette, we had a much longer way to go . . .

Somehow, we always seemed to manage to arrive at the famous Soo locks of Sault Ste. Marie, or the serene lighthouse that marked the unruffled silver beaches of Grand Haven, or the quaint cobblestone village of Holland, Michigan without a scratch. Although occasionally, Lisa, who was not yet old enough to drive, would have to take over, since one of the "new medicines" would often threaten to make my mother fall asleep at the wheel. It was unclear as to which incapable driver caused the most anxiety, and even the usual songs encouraged by Gra's Music Therapy lost their luster when lanes were being crossed within a hair's edge of the next vehicle over. The blurred faces of the other drivers seemed to come within inches of mine in the back seat, taking on bewildered expressions to which I could only shrug as if to say: "Hey, I can't be responsible for this family."

Gra, never one to give up, decided to expose my mother to familiar situations and people of her youth in order to jar my mother's mind back to its original pre-Schizophrenia state. In *this* heroic attempt, she made the rounds of every friend and family member that had shared the social era of the forties with my mother. Somehow Lisa and Jean were excused from these embarrassing sessions (as they were probably gallivanting around the town with their doting Big Sister volunteer). Meanwhile, Theresa, Joe, and I would trail behind Gra and my mother while everyone would pour tea and bring out cookies, all the while attempting to include my mother in conversations of yesterday. My mother, who never lost her natural grace even through the illness, would nod at all the right times, even though we knew she just wanted to get through these awkward moments as quickly as possible. I was always relieved to see everyone pack up the dishes (along with the obvious denial) as we headed out to meet the next Visitation Victim on time.

Family members were always more forgiving, and with this in mind, Gra, bearing baskets of cold fried chicken and potato salad, prepared us for a road trip to visit the Cousins-Once-Removed, that still resided in the old family farmhouse situated in Monroe County. Three sisters whom had never married and were fondly referred to as The Dolls, lived alone in this massive home like a Bad Dollhouse that had mysteriously come to life. Old, yellow, and very wrinkled, they wore ghastly makeup and were no taller than Theresa.

We had heard from all the Great-Aunts that The Dolls' sole occupation was that of Official Funeral Attendees. They had even been known to study the obituaries and show up at the funerals of unknown corpses. My brother had further informed me, that the farmhouse was once a secret meeting place for Communists in the thirties.

Theresa, Joe, and I were assigned our own individual bedrooms in the farmhouse. I had the luxury of a King Size bed with large mahogany posts, along with the unwanted company of chiseled antique dolls wearing hideous baby bonnets, which glared at me from the highboy dresser at the end of the enormous room. Musty doilies were draped around the top of the faded lampshades, and the lingering scent of Communist Ghosts that mooned around the bedroom left an unmistakable glow in the night. That restless evening, I ended up searching the long dark hallways for the room where Theresa was hidden, and gratefully slid into the sheets beside her.

My mother seemed to relish her return back to the hospital after these visits. Secure in an environment that was free of society rules, she was allowed to peacefully coexist with a world that made no demands on her mind. Generous to a fault, all of the gifts of candy and clothing that had been showered on her by Gra were immediately distributed to patient and staff alike. On more than one occasion, a staff member would acknowledge that my mother had a "certain aura" that brought a deep sense of comfort and strength to her day. I was beginning to suspect that God had decided to give my mother away to The State Mental Institutions since they obviously needed an Angel In Their Midst. I gave this theory a lot of thought before I finally confided to Jesus of The Sacred Heart, that I would share her with all the other people of the hospital. Knowing of course, that according to Father Fedewa, this Great Sacrifice was worth at least a Barrel Of Grace in heaven.

Our own return to St. Vincent's after these harrowing weekends was also becoming a welcome relief, since the new liberal changes that were occurring at the new State-run facility were suddenly raining down on us like Manna From Heaven. Outdoor Playtime was extended, and we found ourselves with hours of newfound freedom. Dave would pioneer various projects such as The Toboggan Run that was created by piling at least a dozen picnic tables on top of each other. For weeks, all of us children methodically packed snow into each and every crevice of those tables. Finally, we hauled hundreds of buckets of steaming hot water and poured them on the snow-packed surface.

The day that this Arctic invention was tested, we lined up with much anticipation for what was perceived as The Largest Toboggan Run ever built. It was my turn as I breathlessly climbed the snow packed steps, my eyes skimming the top of the ice encrusted willow trees, as I gathered my courage and proceeded down.

The ride was exhilarating. I felt the cold Michigan air blow furiously across my cheeks, my stocking cap whipping across my neck. This was flying at its finest. The unexpected curves, bumps, and turns that had been engineered for increased speed were introduced at each new corner, as my trusty toboggan skillfully slid through the channeled path. Laughing and braking while dodging the tree that was thoughtfully planted at the end; I spilled out to avoid it and looked up in glee, only to see Sister Cleophas observing me from the window of her new quarters. As I watched, her face seemed to impart a mixed expression of horror at this unladylike sport, along with envy for the fine young man who was quietly stealing our hearts.

June 1968

It was not the usual Summer Camp that year. The nuns of St. Vincent's were to be invited, but were to stay in the Lodge and away from the usual Camp activities. This decision left us children with excited anticipation as to what was to be expected by our new leader. In one of the more curious traditions of St. Vincent's, we girls gathered in the back of the bus to allow the boys to sit in front.

After our Prayer for Protection we all sang in chorus with unbridled enthusiasm one of our favorite songs:

"It's a long long road to Freedom
A-winding steep and high . . .

But when you walk in love with
The wind on your wings
And cover the Earth with
The songs you sing
The miles fly by . . . !

As the speckled blue lake took turns peeking out from the thick green pines, Kathy Sutter and I held hands in silent companionship. After three years Kathy had been released from St. Vincent's and was now living outside of the home with her father.

There had been a joyful reunion at yesterday's annual Ice Cream Social when the Sutter Family came to join in the day's festivities. Since Kathy and I had shared cabins together for the two previous summers, we were tearful about not having the experience again that year. We had decided to ask Mother Vivian if Kathy could be allowed to join us at Summer Camp.

Rosaries in hand, we strolled to the courtyard where the statue of the Virgin Mary stood amidst the colorful tulips—and marveled at the blooms that were a result of our gardening project of the previous fall. For four agonizing hours every morning, Kathy and I had been required to weed the garden in preparation for the seeding of the tulips. Now, as the fresh green sprouts stood in solemn tribute to Our Blessed Mother, we felt that this was the time to ask for the Thimbleful of Grace that surely had been earned on our still-aching knees.

Studying the chiseled nose, blushing cheeks, and gentle blue eyes of the Virgin Mary, we implored with all our might that we might know the blessings of spending camp together.

After ten consecutive Our Fathers, Hail Mary's, and Glory Bees, Kathy and I stood up and felt the strength that could only have come from The Blessed Virgin herself. Now, it was time to seek out the authority figures that held the answers to our Summer Fate.

The approval of Mother Vivian had come swiftly on the heels of Kathy's agreeable Father. We knew without a doubt that the Great Mother Mary had insured our prayers were answered with a suddenness that could only be the result of a true miracle. Holding hands, we ran up to The Pink Room in order to rummage through my dresser for extra summer clothes. After careful thought and considering that it had been a while since I had performed an Act Of Contrition, I solemnly sacrificed my beloved pinstriped pedal pushers to Kathy.

Now, as the Cabins were assigned, Kathy and I leaped for joy as our names were read, knowing that we would once again be summer roommates. I shot Mother Vivian an appreciative glance, and she smiled back at our enthusiasm.

Rolling our sleeping bags over the thin musty mattresses of the cots that were to serve as our temporary beds, we reveled in our good fortune. Just outside the dusty window of our cabin, the lake lapped gently in perfect rhythm with the rustle of the ash trees, whispering promises of adventure and freedom. Kathy unfurled a copy of the latest teen magazine and we paused to admire the bold new wave of miniskirts that wove through the pages with a mysterious lure. Efforts to keep uniform skirts down to an appropriate length were quickly becoming a losing proposition, as young Catholic girls everywhere were keeping their waistbands rolled up. This symbol of rebellion was furiously spreading through the halls of St. Mary's, as more and more students were choosing to bare their knees with a grim defiance of the traditional blue plaid uniform.

"So Kath, what's it really like out there?" I asked.

She pondered the question for a moment. "Actually, I really miss the noise and laughter of St. Vincent's," she replied earnestly. "My father works a lot, and my house seems so quiet . . ."

As Kathy's voice drifted off with her own unspoken thoughts, I hugged my friend and wiped a tear that was forming from the corner of her eye with my navy blue camp shirt. "Come on, Kath—cheer up. At least you get to watch something besides *Lawrence Welk* on Saturday night!"

We both laughed and headed toward the main lodge, pausing to skim a few stones across the glittering, sea green waters.

I was the first to spot the two newly secured rope swings that would only be broken again by the end of the summer. "The Swings!" we proclaimed with excitement, each rushing to claim our favorite. As I perched on the weathered knotted rope, the intoxicating aroma of burning leaves mingled with the fresh lake breeze as it whirled through my hair, and I pumped my feet to generate more speed. The sun was just setting, casting a perfect palate of turquoise and bronze hues through the shadows of the canyon before us.

Kathy and I threw our heads back and laughed with sheer pleasure at the silent taunting of the dark frigid waters beneath us, as if to defy the unspoken fears of an uncertain future.

That evening, after a meal of hamburgers, baked beans, and fresh red tomato slices, we headed down to the cold, blue waters of Lake Alpena. We were all excellent swimmers as learning the art was as necessary as breathing in a State that boasted more water than land. But there was always an air of foreboding about this lake. Its cold frigid waters, with waves that could be ferocious in the frequent summer storms, were notorious in the Upper Peninsula region for turning even the strongest Michigan sailors to mush. Thus, the lake was respected and feared at the same time.

I ventured near the hot, flickering fire and inhaled the smoky smells of leaves, while peeking at the "new boy" with the long brown eyes and fringed black eyelashes. Kathy and I had both recently wondered what a first kiss would be like, and as I observed the curve of Tommy Porter's lips, I wondered if Frances Ayala had really stuck her tongue into one of the boys' mouths while on Dish-washing Duty. With a hushed tone and a great air of knowledge, she declared to Kathy and me that this was known as a French Kiss, and that *we* would probably never know the wonders of its mystery.

After finding the perfect stick and roasting my marshmallow to a brown, gooey consistency, I took a seat near Kathy in one of the old wooden bleachers.

Dave was telling a Ghost Story and all had become transfixed as his voice rose above the wind, whispering the horrors of The Ghost of Lake Alpena. "As the Legend was told . . ." Dave began, huddling down near the youngest children. The soft lapping of the nearby waves, mixed with the snap and crackle of burning twigs. Somewhere in the distance a melancholy whippoorwill offered a haunting background melody, while the Ghost of Lake Alpena seemed to be hovering discreetly nearby. .

According to Dave, it was over one hundred years ago when Alpena and the very place where we were now sitting was just a small lumber camp. During this time, a young maiden was quietly nurturing an unrequited love for one of the strong young lumberjacks. In desperation, she decided to jump in the water as a ploy for his attention. Not understanding the strong currents of the water, she was pulled away by the undertow, never having the opportunity to express her true feelings. Now, she was known to still emerge from the Lake in anguish, searching in vain for her beloved lumberjack. As Fate Would Have It however, the poor lumberjack just happened to have been beheaded by a fallen tree, shortly after the fair maidens death—and would never know of this undying love.

As I dwelled on this distinct possibility, I could vividly imagine the young distressed woman, with lips that would never know a kiss . . . and vowed right then to make kissing Tommy's lips a summer goal.

Suddenly, in the calm of the evening waters, I imagined I saw a ripple of water moving gently in the breeze. As I watched with increasingly larger eyes, the ripple became a circle, and it was apparent that something was indeed moving about ten feet from the water's edge. Could it be a fish swimming that close to the shore?

A bit of white was seen creeping out of the water, and as I watched in horror, a transparent figure surfaced from the Lake and was heading toward our bleachers. A sinister white floating mass that was wailing in anguish and distress. The Ghost of Lake Alpena!

I turned to run, stumbling up the wooden bleachers, breathlessly taking them three rows at a time, my body responding with a supernatural speed that only great fear can generate.

Upon entering the forbidden cabin of the makeshift convent without knocking, I vaguely heard the saxophone players ringing from the television as Lawrence Welk was seducing the nuns with their favorite Saturday night program. Catapulting into the arms of Mother Vivian, I gasped the details of the camp inhabited by the Ghost of Lake Alpena. Dave said so, and I had just seen her myself. The interruption was suddenly forgiven, as the room of nuns responded with clucking sounds of amusement.

Gathering me in her arms, Mother Vivian informed me that Dave had convinced one of the boys to crouch in the lake, draped with a sheet until just the right moment. I smelled the crisp clean starch of her habit, and fingered the crucifix that hung around her neck as she awkwardly smoothed my hair, seeming to realize that I needed more than she could give.

My guardian angel must have made a rare personal visit that night, because Mother Vivian herself gently woke me from sleep the next morning, and with a quiet smile on her lips, led me back to the Lodge. There, underneath the tall pine tree where Kathy had I had earnestly scratched our initials on the bark, stood my daddy! He had decided to take a "much-needed" fishing trip and would be staying at the camp with us for a week.

Running into his arms for a hug, I put my small hand into his large, comforting one. As I led him through the camp, cheerily chatting and pointing out the beauty of the wilderness, I reveled in God's goodness and the fact that I was the first of my siblings to know of this delicious surprise.

When I looked back to see Mother Vivian with that same small smile fondly looking after us, it occurred to me that those lips were exact replicas of that of the Statue of the Blessed Virgin Mary. I would include ten Guardian Angel Prayers to my growing evening repertoire now, as it was apparent that she was indeed in my midst. Bowing my head, I silently said one now:

Guardian Angel
My Guardian Dear
To Whom God's love
Commits me near
Ever This Day
Be at my Side
To Light, to Guard, to Rule and To Guide
Amen

Tracing my earlier steps through the woods, I decided to share "The Secret Garden" with my father, as the perfect place to view the morning sunrise. Only Kathy Sutter and I knew of this secluded hide-a-way near the creek where we shared giggles, prayers, and dreams of the alluring first kiss that would be our ultimate destiny.

Discovering this sacred spot required scrambling over large white boulders and I patiently waited for my father who seemed to be moving a little more slowly these days. I stopped to take in the overwhelming scent of fresh pine that exuded throughout the blue spruce path, as the scarlet wings of a cardinal perched on a branch in quiet acceptance of our approach.

I was just about to hurdle the last boulder, which would reveal a magnificent green meadow that bordered the creek, when I heard the crisp sounds of crackling branches. My father, slightly out of breath, was catching up to me as I observed Tommy Porter pensively making his way out of the meadow. I fought down the mixed emotions of resentment for this invasion of my special place, with the familiar new excitement that seemed to occur with each encounter of this interesting boy. As I made the introduction, my father seemed to visibly retreat as he sternly looked at us with a questioning instinct that thickened the pine-filled air.

I sympathized with Tommy who stood in a military pose in response to the older man's inspection. His final appraisal seemed to suggest Tommy would never be good enough for his revered daughter.

Briefly struggling with the urge to defend Tommy's character during this unspoken accusation, I decided instead to take my father's hand and continue our private walk. It was only after glancing back, that I saw Tommy's beautiful brown eyes promise the unspoken certainty of a shared kiss in the seclusion of our mutual secret place.

As we surveyed the beauty of the beckoning green meadow from the final boulder, I slowly released my father's hand, and took a joyful leap into the wide blue horizon.

That evening's dinner festivities seemed a little more colorful than usual, as if staged for the benefit of my father. Sister Cleophas was gushing about the merits of each child with a feigned enthusiasm that suggested she knew each of us on an intimate basis. The severe frown that seemed a natural part of her expression had softened into a contrast of giggling femininity. My father, dressed in a rugged plaid shirt and freshly ironed slacks, was responding with the gentle manners of a handsome man who is aware of his effect on women. Kathy and I exchanged looks at the table and rolled our eyes with amusement. I couldn't help but sympathize with the fumbling nun however, since even her brightest fantasies would not produce a courtship in the lifelong vow of celibacy.

I was just cutting off the chocolate section of my Neapolitan ice cream when there was a surprise announcement: We children would be under the direct supervision of a new Nun in Training who would be doing her internship that summer at St. Vincent's. Louise wore a simple white blouse and navy blue skirt that seemed much more hip than the cumbersome black habit that she would eventually don. Vivacious and energetic, she had arrived at the Lake with all of her worldly belongings: one small blue suitcase and a guitar in a battered black case. Our very own Singing Nun!

The next morning, we began the day with a nature hike that had been scheduled by Louise. The white birch trees were in sharp contrast to the aqua blue of the unusually calm waters, and Louise stopped to pick a mustard yellow wildflower, which she daintily placed behind her ear. We children chattered uncontrollably with this new intern who seemed to have fallen down from Heaven as a blissful gift of reprieve from the stern Sister Cleophas.

Later that day, we all gathered under one of the great willow trees that towered over the lake shore. The elegant branches seemed to bow into a graceful emerald canopy, as if to humbly offer its filtered protection from the sun. The stagnant August air was creating the perfect atmosphere for ants, and I slapped one now as he threatened to ride up the crotch of my white hot pants. I was proud of my persistent political abilities that had allowed everyone to indulge in a much more interesting Play Wardrobe.

Louise opened the worn black guitar case and lovingly caressed the strings as we observed every detail with delight. Soon a melody of song burst forward from her throat, and we were transfixed at the sweetness of sound that pulsated without warning. "Please, Louise, sing another song," we demanded, as she plucked at the chords with a lilting voice that seemed to carry into the breeze like a beautiful songbird;

"Where have all the flowers gone . . ."

And with blissful ignorance of the growing events of the Vietnam War, we children joined in with a naïve response to the changing times.

"Long time passing. . . ."

The boys were all smitten, and on more than one occasion as we would be engaged in the spirited conversations that Louise seemed to encourage, they would candidly inquire, "Why in the world do you want to become a nun?" Her pale blue eyes would crinkle with good humor as she would simply explain that she loved the Lord.

Dave and Louise seemed to strike up a perfect combination of young good looks and the determination that each shared to make the most of our days at St. Vincent's. But as the summer wore on, there seemed to be a new glimmer of admiration for each other that was becoming increasingly obvious.

Kathy and I were sauntering back from the Lodge after an afternoon session of Arts and Crafts when we both heard the desperate cries of our beloved Louise. Apparently, Dave had convinced the boys to throw her into the lake, clothes and all. As we watched Louise helplessly traipsing back to shore through the heavy current of the waves, we turned our eyes away with compassion. Louise was desperately trying to remain in good spirits while the white blouse of her uniform was clinging to her Nun Bra. At that very moment, Debbie Stauffer appeared from beneath the burnt umber of a maple tree, book in hand, and Kathy and I suppressed giggles as we watched the older girl quietly study the fuller form of Louise. An unmistakable spark of jealousy flashed from Debbie's eyes before she noticed Kathy and me, and scurried away in embarrassment.

Meanwhile, my heart went out to Louise as she attempted to pull the clinging wet white blouse away from the voluptuous curves of her breasts, but not before twenty curious little white boys and one particularly entranced young man had taken full inventory. "Leave it to Dave to let the boys do his Dirty Work," I muttered to Kathy, who was collecting her own thoughts of the situation.

"To think Nuns actually have Boobs," Kathy marveled. "Why would God give those things to people that don't plan on using them?" We both contemplated this fact for a moment before we decided that God must have bestowed Nuns with Boobs in order to see if they could resist Temptation.

"After all," I confided to Kathy, "it was only after Adam screwed up so bad in the Garden, that God forced all the boys to wear those snakes around for Life." We walked back to our cabin in silence after that, content to know that there *was indeed* Justice In Our World.

That summer proved to be more challenging than usual, as we fought to keep up with the eternal mischief of Dave and the boys. Louise was the new advocate in defending our cause, but she also seemed to weaken under the undeniable charisma of Dave.

This was indeed the case one rainy afternoon when the boys presented us with a gift that they had discovered during their morning hike. A huge snapping turtle bearing a miserable, defeated expression and tied by a thick rope was led to the evening fireside. Dave was boasting that it was only because of the talents of Men as Providers, that we helpless women would survive in the vast wilderness of the great outdoors. Louise, who had not been entirely sheltered from the budding Women's Lib Movement, was quick to object.

Wrapping the rope around the wrinkled green neck of this enormous turtle, Dave declared a tug of war, as proof that the men would always be the dominant force of our newly evolving world. To my horror, Louise took Dave up on this challenge, as it was agreed that the losing team would have to make Turtle Soup for dinner.

Closing my eyes tightly, I took my portion of the rope, since there did not seem to be a clear way out of this situation. And with a quick apology to the turtle and any of his unsuspecting family members—I pulled in tandem with twenty-nine other little girls who were sure that the honor of their entire gender was at stake.

The rope began to shred in my red welting hands as the final tug sent both sides sprawling. Refusing to look at the remnants of our innocent hostage, I made my way back to my cabin with a prayer to God for the Mortal Sin that we had just committed.

That evening, fearing the prospect of the Turtle Soup appetizer, I left the fireside early with gnawing pains of hunger and murder weighing on my consciousness. Taking the route of The Secret Garden, I was once again surprised to encounter Tommy in quiet reflection at the creek. He patted the ground in a friendly gesture, and I slid in beside him with an attempt to remain calm. The dark lashes framed his brown eyes like a black smudge of coal, and they seemed to probe into mine with a desire to know more.

"What in the world were they thinking with that poor turtle?" I asked Tommy in an effort to Break The Ice. He smiled, tenderly taking my hand in his own warm palm. I panicked just for a moment as I fought to remember exactly how Kathy had taught me to lace my fingers, should this very opportunity arise. But Tommy made it all appear easy as he tightened my hand into his and leaned over to kiss me. It was a short kiss, but held all the magic that was expected, and I caught my breath with sheer surprise. He smiled, and brushing my hair gently from my cheek, ventured forth with a more courageous effort the second time around. I blushed as his tongue seemed to hold the same inquiring tone of the magnetic eyes. Pulling away, while simultaneously taking a mental photograph of the details of this moment for my report to Frances, I shyly lowered my eyes to the ground.

"I have to go," I said. Tommy brushed my breast with his hand as a reluctant response to my announcement. It seemed such an innocent gesture that I pretended not to notice. I quickly stepped back from the tumbling brush, while pushing down the strong desire to lie beside this strange boy as a gift of gratitude for stirring my soul. The crickets were just beginning their evening song as I waved goodbye and quietly headed back to the cabin.

After my own experience of suppressed passions, I was not surprised when it was announced that Louise would give up her Residency that summer. It was determined that there had been a new direction in the Lord's path for Louise–and she would no longer be continuing her walk as a Sister of Christ. Ironically, this news came on the heels of Dave's new job transfer and there were many tearful goodbyes as each child's heart went out to the couple who had seasoned our days with laughter and adventure.

The melody of Louise's guitar and Dave's contagious laugh seemed to fade into the background like a hazy mist. Our beloved songbirds had found another way Home—and life as one curious twelve-year-old knew it took on a softer but wiser glow.

14

September 1969

I n an effort to shore up its dissolving teen-age demograph-
ics, the Catholic Church was emerging with a new identity
as the turbulent sixties were coming to a close. Suddenly,
the Dress Code at St. Mary's Elementary included blue
jeans and Long Hair, to the horror of my father, while guitar masses
complete with the English Language were introduced as a substi-
tute to the much rehearsed Latin phrases of more archaic times.
Simon and Garfunkel were embraced into the church as a symbol
of its newfound coolness, a strategy that as my father pointed out
seemed a little puzzling, considering that the two popular musi-
cians were actually Jewish boys from the Bronx.

After relentless political persuasion to all the right sources, I was selected to serve as one of the first Altar Girls in the Church, to the dismay of my brother who thought women should never have a place at the Altar. And as proof that the never-ending elementary days were behind me, I had just received the Holy Sacrament of Confirmation. Kneeling before the red gown of the Cardinal who was flown in just for the occasion, I stoically received the slap on my cheek as a new name was given to me, "Catherine," which was part of the ritual of becoming a "Soldier of Christ." This seemed a relatively simple oath, since military environments had been my only way of life, and I was looking forward to the future with an enthusiasm that was blossoming as quickly as the new bras being donned everywhere by my female classmates.

It was with this snappy new attitude that I studied the list of Commandments that were inscribed on the stone plaques of each of the Stations of the Cross during Friday afternoon Confession. For six of my Catholic school years, I had recited the same two sins on a weekly basis in the following order: "I Lied and I Fought with My Brothers and Sisters." Determined to carve out a new identity for myself, I decided that my usual declarations had become too routine, and would have to be replaced with a sin that was a little more glamorous. Slowly using the process of elimination, I lingered on "Thou Shalt not Kill," but realized that from a Priest's perspective, chopping a worm into nine pieces to see if he lived might be pardoned for its educational value. Finally, I decided on "Thou Shalt not commit Adultery," since anything to do with Adults would only confirm my new Status Quo.

Just as I was shifting my throbbing knees to prevent the Kneeling Fungus that Jean had warned me about, the light turned green above the confessional. Terry Taylor was making her way to the pew with a glazed look that suggested a longer-than-usual Penance: a sure sign of a newly ordained Priest. I pushed back the heavy burgundy velvet drapes and peered into the darkness of the musty booth. Pressing my knees into the bench just as the blood had started circulating in them again, I watched the green light turn to red indicating that the booth was occupied by a sinner in repentance.

The screen window connecting my booth to the One who was in command of my fate slowly slid open, and I observed the silhouette of the dominant figure, who in that moment, held all the power to resolve my many sins. "Bless me Father, for I have Sinned," I began. "My last confession was: (standard answer) one week ago."

"What is your Sin?" the Shadow boomed as he beckoned me to come closer.

Gathering my courage for the big announcement, I declared proudly, "I fought with my brother and sisters and I committed Adultery."

There was a silence on the other side of the screen and I began to squirm just as my knees began experiencing the alarming Pins and Needles sensation that was, as Jean had quietly explained it, a distinct Side Effect of the dreaded Kneeling Fungus.

"What did you say?" the Shadow inquired with what seemed a whisper compared to his original introduction.

In a weakened version of the original tone that I had so carefully delivered, I repeated my statement.

"What exactly did you do when you committed Adultery?" he inquired.

Now I knew I had bitten off more than I could chew, since I had no clue what the word Adultery meant. But I proceeded with another question in order to obtain more information, as they were teaching us in Journalism Class. "What do you think I mean?" I asked.

"Well, for instance, did you take off your pants?"

Okay, now I was in for it. How was I going to get out of this one? Lying about a series of Lies would net me no less than one thousand Our Fathers, five hundred Hail Mary's and two hundred and fifty Glory BEES as my Penance. So, taking a deep breath and crossing my fingers behind my back while thanking the Lord for making Confessional booths dark for just this purpose, I replied, "Yes, I took off my pants."

"Tell me, what happened next?" The Shadow pursued in a hushed tone. "Did you touch your Private Parts?"

I wondered if he meant the private parts that my brother could never see, and silently wished that I had selected a less-complicated commandment. "Yes, I guess I touched my Private Parts" was the answer that I thought he was looking for.

The young voice slowly digested this information. Just as I was thinking it wouldn't be so bad to just be swallowed up and buried in that box, saving my father the cost of a coffin, there was an onslaught of more curious questions. I quickly determined that it would be better to agree with everything than to acknowledge my ignorance of the subject and continued to confess that yes, just like Mary Magdalene, MY needs could never be satiated.

"Well, then, you have committed a Mortal Sin. This will require that you pray here in the Confessional for your Penance." I recited the familiar words of my Sentence and quickly left the confessional, managing to avoid all the eyes that seemed to linger on me in judgment for my unusually long stay. I put in an extra fervent prayer that God would not send me to Purgatory forever, and at the same time wondered about the awkward silence that had leapt out behind that dark screen as I recited my Penance. If God was indeed sending that Priest as his Messenger, I certainly did not know why he needed so many details. Pushing the incident behind me, I vowed that the only one that I would ever share the unusual behavior of that Priest with would be St. Peter himself.

The sounds of rain pattered on the window as I peered into the darkness of the cemetery, perhaps for the hundredth time wondering how the Dead People avoided getting wet underground. Jean had told me that they escaped from their graves and gathered together for parties under the Old Oak Tree late at night, and they all had white luminescent umbrellas just for these occasions. Although lately, lots of things Jean had told me in the past were beginning to raise questions in my mind.

Suddenly, I heard the distinct sounds of happy voices and giggling arising from the Blue Room. An unheard of distraction after Final Lights Outs. After confirming that my roommates were asleep, I made the decision to venture into the hallway to peer into the doorway of The Blue Room. There, dripping with rainwater and looking exactly like a drowned rat, was Debbie Stauffer.

Debbie had been One Of The Fortunate Few to have left St. Vincent's, but only after her father had decided to marry her mother in order to share custody. This huge sacrifice was accomplished; Debbie had preened, strictly so her father could have access to his cherished daughter again. It struck me that Debbie was missing the whole point that fifteen years of age was the maximum allowed for the children of St. Vincent's, and other arrangements were forced to be made. I also wondered again why fathers were not given custody of their children. Weren't they supposed to be the responsible ones? I gazed in awe at my first encounter of a person who had left the Home, only to actually return to the Scene of the Crime.

The girls from the Blue Room were gathered around Debbie, pressing her with questions. Debbie had actually had the opportunity to go to Woodstock! A fact that had my sister Lisa positively dripping with envy. "Over 500,000 people were there," Debbie bragged to those of us fortunate enough to be in her presence. "My uncle and I took his old Volkswagen Van, painted it aqua blue just for the occasion, and drove all the way to Bethel, New York for three glorious days." She went on to admit that the fun was somewhat dampened from the torrents of mud and rain that poured down on the festival, during which time Debbie lost her uncle and spent much of the afternoon watching something called Canned Heat on the shoulders of an exuberant young Rock and Roller.

Savoring the next news, Debbie slowly conveyed the information that she had smoked her first joint right there at Woodstock, and was now officially a Flower Child. Her parents were still struggling with this new identity, but Debbie had informed them that she was changed forever. After a harrowing evening of arguing this point with her parents, Debbie had actually left her home in tears and HITCHIKED to St. Vincent's. This particular piece of information had Leatrice doubled up with laughter for the sheer horror that would befall Cleophas should she discover the truth. "Girl, I *know* you *got* to be crazy to come here of all places!" Leatrice snickered, shaking her head in appreciation.

As if to Read Her Mind, Sister Cleophas appeared from her new quarters, with the pretense of carrying fresh linens in her arms. I had to give her credit for finding a convenient prop in order to discover what all the commotion was about. A white wash cloth drifted lazily to the floor, as the fragile nun stopped in her tracks to absorb the scene before her. I squinted from my post in the darkened hallway with an attempt to take in this unexpected drama from Sister Cleophas's eyes.

Debbie's long brown hair had a perfectly straight part which was currently hanging in moist strands down her back. She wore a faded jean jacket, on the back of which was painted a design of what looked like green tobacco. Someone with a worse sewing hand than my own had crudely sewn the words, "See Me, Roll Me, Smoke Me" in purple thread. Debbie's legendary large boobs hung out of a gauzy crème colored blouse that was apparently tied in the back by two long strings. She was wearing long bellbottom jeans that were soaked to the point of squeaking. The fabric parachuted from her knees with various pieces of denim that had been sewn together to create two large bell shapes that cascaded to her feet. It was here that I caught the reason for the horror on Sister Cleophas's face.

"You're barefoot?" she feebly exclaimed from her position in the doorway. Debbie giggled nervously as she tried to hide her feet under the fabric of the jeans. The hem of her jeans was so long, it struck me that her attempts to cover up them up were almost successful. Sister Cleophas however, would notice every drip of water as it cascaded onto the freshly polished floors, but because her role of authority was unclear in this situation, the tired nun chose to remain silent.

Choosing to take advantage of the moment, Debbie went on to shock Sister Cleophas with more colorful tales of her travels to Woodstock, after which time, the nun had to finally drop into her old rocking chair, untying a shoe and kneading her foot as she observed the dismal results of her child rearing efforts. With a smile of defeat, she silently rocked and allowed us the pleasure of another hour of chatting before escorting Debbie back to the lobby. There seemed to be in the old nun's halting walk through the polished hallways, a small note of surrender to the new ways of the world. It was said that Cleophas had actually gotten into her old jar of coins, and counted out just enough money to pay for Debbie's cab ride home that night. As for the rest of us, we turned into bed with visions of Rock Concerts, pastel colored vans, and the Taste Of Freedom ringing through our ears long after Debbie had driven off into the storm weary streets of Lansing. The seventies were upon us and the Times . . . They Were a Changin.'

October 1969

The old Mackinac Point lighthouse winked at me with unmistakable pity, as I surrendered to the swirling leaves of a turquoise sky with a newly reformed attitude of submission. Gra was still bent on finding a travel-inspired solution to my mother's progressively worse mental illness. Our latest Sunday excursions were now riddled not only with the random effects of my mother's revolutionary pre-seventy drugs, but the combustible chemistry of five pre-adolescent children. The whole thing made for a lethal combination of Hormonal Hell.

The latest prescription marvels had "graciously" brought new side affects, to the already colorful mix of my mothers ever changing conduct. Thanks to the recent wonder drugs of certain pharmaceutical companies, we could now look forward to unexpected public displays of unpredictable behavior, peppered with occasional outbursts of senseless conversation.

Furthermore, just to add to the pressure, my mother acquired a taste for sporadic impulses that we were simply required to go along with. Sometimes these requests would involve stopping at a restaurant for a beer and some peanuts, during which time we would all cringe in embarrassment while my mother fired a medley of confusing questions at our waiter. And then in a welcome rendition of a once brilliant personality, she would suddenly relapse into flawless, intelligent conversation. "Have you ever been to the Moulin Rouge, my dear?" she would inquire of a wary staff member who by this time would be weighing all of us with a certain suspicion for our own mental stability.

With an astounding accuracy for historical details, my mother would go on to relay a delightful and precise account of an adventurous trip that was taken to Paris in her twenties, intertwined with an accurate biography of the great composers of its time. We all suspected that my mother took more than a little pleasure in exposing random pieces of her unusual intelligence, purely to provoke a small dose of Shock Value to the unsuspecting souls who crossed her path. And sometimes, when she would appear momentarily normal, I couldn't help but imagine that she was just Faking It, all this time. My sister Lisa did nothing to alleviate my fears, and instead marveled that this formula might actually have been a pretty brilliant attempt on my mother's part to have simply, "Checked Out."

Either way, I had nothing to lose by slipping into compliance, rather than admitting total defeat. The idea of going back to St. Vincent's on Sunday evenings was even beginning to sound more appealing than these anguishing road trips. In fact, later that evening, the Pink Room was planning to stage our own version of *American Bandstand* for the girls in The Blue Room, and I couldn't wait to try out my new moves for everyone. Leatrice had even shared some of her own techniques from *The Funky Chicken* with me, and had graciously admitted that for A White Girl, I had been blessed with surprisingly good rhythm.

My sister Jean was convinced that it was the very answer to her prayers—a present sent from *her* own guardian angel. We were leaving St. Vincent's on October fifth, her fourteenth birthday!

As we piled into the aging Oldsmobile, the five of us children were lighthearted and giddy with anticipation about the priceless freedom awaiting us. Lisa had just turned fifteen, and since it was agreed to never separate us as siblings, we were released to my father from the court on a full-time custody basis. A final gift of separation from the Catholic Church, who had imposed on our family circumstances over the years like a meddling Stepparent.

Mother Vivian led us out to the parking lot and said a final goodbye to each of us, giving me a warm hug. The formal Catholic Church habit had recently been exchanged for a shapely, black and white dress that clung to her knee, subtly revealing the femininity that had been so closely guarded over the years. The newly rounded breasts and curves of the nuns seemed to coincide with a universal exchange of liberating attitudes and interests. Thus, the boundaries of solitude were lifted as these Sisters of Christ were suddenly brought outside the convents and into public places everywhere. It was as if a country of suppressed third-world women were finally coming out of hiding. I secretly wondered if our generation's persistence in defying authority with fashionable uniform lengths was somehow responsible for this desperately needed wardrobe update in the Catholic Church.

I took a final sniff of the familiar starch through watery eyes that caused the sparkle of her silver cross to blur. "Now, now," Mother Vivian said as she gave my shoulders a final squeeze. "I want to hear nothing but good reports from your father," she announced to the rest of us. Looking over her shoulder and ignoring my impatient older sister, who was stepping on my toe in an effort to Get On With Her Life, I suddenly saw a head bobbing in the open window of the reception area. Mother Vivian smiled and allowed Leatrice through the forbidden open doors to say a final goodbye.

Leatrice's familiar grin and the unkempt wig sporting a pink comb was suddenly standing before us. Her navy blue uniform was hanging in the telltale fashion of a skirt that had been too quickly adjusted back to its proper length. The SMS patch that stood for Saint Mary's School was peeled from too many washings, and as usual the navy blue socks were rolled down to her thin ankles. We all laughed as Leatrice gave us the expression that said, "Where are all my white sisters going without me?" Tears came to our eyes as we hugged our friend, who truly had become a member of The Peters Clan. It was difficult to comprehend that Leatrice would be gone from our lives forever.

The tall willow trees that graced the long curved driveway seemed to nod in farewell, as if they had known all along the exact moment of our final departure from St. Vincent's. My father slowly drove past the large iron entrance gate and we heard the familiar creak behind us. This time, however, the noise seemed amplified, as if announcing to the world the formal arrival of five innocent debutantes entering unfamiliar, yet exciting new territory. I bid a solemn farewell to my imaginary friends at the cemetery, as the Old Oak unfurled a gnarled hand to wave goodbye to me in the brisk October wind.

December 1969

I expertly slung my tied skates over my shoulders and patiently waited for Theresa to return from the Hothouse with our hot chocolate. My feet were numb with relief, as we had skated longer than usual that evening. Theresa appeared flushed and excited as she handed me the steamy cup of cocoa. We were both proud of ourselves for finally mastering the art of skating backward. The Toboggan Run at Comstock Park was quiet that evening as my little sister and I headed home in quiet companionship.

A perfect full moon loomed ahead of us, casting a rosy blush around the entwined profile of Jean and her new boyfriend, Ray

Alicia, as they sauntered ahead, immersed in their own little world.

Personally, I was still miffed from the brutal ear piercing that I was forced to endure for the sake of Jean's *latest* new enterprise. As no other volunteers were present during this moment of enlightenment, I had found myself perched on a chair in front of the yard of our new home, while my sister pressed two bitterly cold ice cubes on my lobes. Jean then proceeded to cheerfully drive a reluctant needle completely through my earlobe, all the while demonstrating to the captivated neighborhood children that they too, could enjoy the luxury of pierced ears, for a special one time rate of two dollars. It would not have been so bad if my ears were completely numb before the piercing had taken place. But Jean didn't even Miss A Beat in her presentation, as she gracefully sopped the oozing blood with little round cotton balls, as if it were all part of the plan.

Later, upon seeing the haphazard holes in my mangled ears, my father was livid. "Your sister, will not be pierced in front of the neighbors like a sacrificial lamb," he stormed.

"But Dad," Jean had argued sweetly, "Annie doesn't even have to pay me the two dollars until her next babysitting job."

Nursing my swollen earlobes, I quietly decided that I would wait for another time to seek my revenge, even though at the moment, I was dying to loudly announce that Jean was wearing tissue paper in her bra, and was really only a size 32A.

Ray carried Jean's skates in one arm while, the other lay gently across her shoulder in a protective embrace. Jean had already confided to me that just the other night, Ray had kissed her while they were walking home from the park, and then had spun around on his heels, and promptly ran away. "Ray peeled out of there like he saw a ghost!" Jean said with a perplexed frown on her brow. From the looks of things, Ray had wasted no time in finding his way back.

Lisa had also found a certain interest in Ray's older brother

Rick, and the four of them were meeting at the movies, and at church on a regular basis. My father was actually quite fond of the brothers, and Ray had even gone so far as to Take a Drive with him one evening, "He actually told Dad that someday he would have me as his wife," Jean had explained to me in a hushed whisper of horror.

Ray's courageous request had earned the respect of all of us after that–since according to my father "There had never been a Puerto Rican President." Apparently, Ray had convinced my father that he would even go so far as to become President, if it meant having my sister's hand in marriage.

Theresa and I still shared the same bunk beds of our youth in a brand new home that my father had purchased on the south side of the city. The old house on Michigan Avenue had been demolished to make way for future revitalization efforts. Felix the cat, had become mangier over the years, and had permanent scars, along with a few mangled teeth from frequent neighborhood fights in which he had to reclaim his "cathood"–but nevertheless generously allowed me to share *his* bed. Two dog-eared posters of Bobby Sherman and David Cassidy were perched on our walls along with a new black light which had been smuggled from Joe's room–causing their chiseled white teeth to radiate with a warm sensual glow after my father had made his good night rounds. I just knew that once Bobby finally discovered that we had changed addresses–he would soon find his way to our new home to claim *me* as his One and Only True Love.

Meanwhile, it appeared from a distance that Jean was about to receive her evening kiss in full view of all of us who walked home from the park. Standing on her toes, and daintily kicking one foot up just like they did in the movies, my sister pursed her lips in anticipation of another passionate kiss from Ray. This time however, he merely offered her a wifely peck on the cheek, which would be guaranteed to leave Jean even more puzzled about his Real Motives. I noticed that Ray's leather cap was perched on his head rather jauntily, and he whistled a confident little tune while waving goodbye to Theresa and I before heading off to the north side of town.

"Wait up!" Theresa called out to Jean who looked like she was purposely trying to lose us. Jean motioned for us to be quiet, as she dove into the bushes in front of our house. Theresa and I laughed as we peered behind the shrubbery to watch Jean wiggle out of the blue jeans that were forbidden in our home, quickly changing into the conservative slacks that my father would approve of. Lisa and Jean had a whole wardrobe of blue jeans and makeup stashed in the bushes, just for these occasions.

"You better get rid of that blue eye shadow," I reminded her, shocked at my own generosity of spirit. If nothing else, my Grace Points were quickly accelerating. Jean gave me a look of gratitude for this important cue, as she furiously rubbed her eyelids for any obvious evidence.

While Lisa had gone on to Bigger and Better Things, at Catholic Central High School, I gratefully welcomed a treasure chest of freedoms at St. Casimir, the new Catholic Junior High that Jean, Joe and I were attending. Meanwhile, Theresa was basking in her newfound popularity at Holy Cross, and was busy celebrating her role as Leading Angel in the school play.

Gone were the days of relentless routines, as slumber parties that highlighted amusing games of Twister, complete with pepperoni pizzas and awkward-but-interesting dances, were just some of the new activities of this previously distant world. My father, sensitive to the natural fashion instincts of four teenage girls, allowed us to indulge our senses with a clothing allowance of one hundred dollars each at *Maurice's* boutique store. As a bonus, I saw my wardrobe quadruple as The Pile, free from the rigid standards of St. Vincent's dress codes, became transformed into a delightful new medley of leather belts and cropped shorts. My father continued to be puzzled as to why we needed the heavy belts to hold up shorts that were "barely there," but nevertheless, generously Looked The Other Way when Jean and I appeared in the latest new Sizzle Dresses for school one morning. Even though as Joe pointed out, to my complete embarrassment, that it was a really good thing there were coordinating underpants for our shockingly short dresses.

"Well, *you're* just lucky there's not a match around!" I had answered in kind. After all, Joe had been strutting around all morning, Proud As A Peacock in his new polyester Leisure Suit, which was clearly marked "Highly Flammable" on the label.

My father did his best not to appear overwhelmed, although looking back, the daunting task of raising five teen-age children must have been quite intimidating. But the learned discipline that had been imposed on us by St. Vincent's did not go unearned, as each child willingly jumped in to schedule cooking and cleaning chores without much prodding on my father's part.

Another more difficult rule that was established in our motherless household was The Mandatory 5 o'clock Dinner. Jean and Lisa had the assigned duties of cooking the evening meal, a responsibility that too often interfered with their growing social lives. Too often, these efforts resulted in underdone chicken pot pies, meat loaf that bore a suspicious resemblance to our dog's Gravy Train, and side dishes of Spam that were a distinct afterthought. As a diabetic, my father insisted that the Dinner should consist of all the five basic food groups, and so the girls attempted to appease his logic rather than our taste buds. For instance, even after Thanksgiving was long gone, the untouched cranberry sauce had continued to appear at the dinner table in the same blue dish. With those few exceptions, our lives took on the normalcy that had always been taken for granted by our peers. Sunday mornings were filled once again with the traditions of Mass at St. Mary's, followed by a pancake breakfast. My father had just purchased a 1969 Oldsmobile Station Wagon, and the twangy country music that he playfully forced on us was politely endured, even as we pressed our hands in agony over our tender new rock-and-roll ears. The new car proved to be useful for more than transportation however, as we all donned flannel pajamas and headed for the *Starlight Drive-In*.

This meant that all five children, along with a friend or two, would vertically nestle in the back of the wagon like sardines in a tin can. My father, always one to tap into our adventurous side, would offer us the option of sneaking in through the cornfield, or entering through the more ethical way of paying. Joe and I of course, always opted for the cornfield, even though it meant climbing a large, barbed-wire fence as my brother would warn of the bloodhounds that were hot on our path.

The crackling, muffled speakers and frigid night air that crept into the open car window did not always prove to be the most ideal movie setting. The concession stand was always a nice distraction, even though it meant climbing out of the station wagon over various limbs and loud objections. Driving home at this unusually late hour, my father would be treated with a rare gift of silence as five weary teen-agers tumbled into bed, grateful for the well-thought-out pajama plan. It was as if the few lost years of our youth were merely a peculiar dream.

During this time, my mother would sometimes be released from the latest institution for a Saturday afternoon visit. Her gentle aqua eyes would roam the room, only to light on each of us with the depth of individual love that only a child can really fathom.

My father intuitively knew how to communicate with my mother at her level, and sometimes they would share an occasional beer together before dinner. At my repeated urgings, he even took all the right precautions against the inevitable House Fire that I was sure would be the fate of our household as he carefully disposed of the smoldering cigarettes with quiet aplomb.

Fascinated, I would watch him gently converse with her as a human being, wife, and mother, rather than the Patient Label my mother now wore like a badge of the State Psychiatric System.

I couldn't help but wonder if my father missed those earlier carefree days of a beer and a cigarette which were once enjoyed in the lighthearted moments of young love, instead of the coping mechanism that they had become.

"Oh, Bill," my mother would laugh, as he chided her with the type of outrageous humor that he knew she would respond to.

As welcome fragments of my mother's long lost laughter tinkled throughout our home, these doses of humor seemed to provide more immediate results than all those big Chemical Laboratories combined.

And sometimes in those fleeting moments, the eyes of my parents would connect with an acceptance and curiosity that suggested the obvious; if the Destiny that had once brought them together had simply chosen another path, how different their lives might have been.

Latching on to the daughters of Doctors and Architects in my ever popular new friendships, I quickly discovered how to maneuver my way into guest invitations that included ski trips and lake houses. And, as my circle of friends widened, I continued to observe the traditions of these families who were somehow not as "normal" as I would have hoped. As part of my obsessive nature to inspect each of the medicine cabinets in these recurring vacation homes, I could not help but notice that everyone carried the same medicine bottles which were neatly lined on the shelves. It seemed odd that all the suburban mothers of the day seemed to have come down with the same virus at once. It was only while assisting at the parties given by my friend's mothers that I overheard the medicine fondly referred to as *Mothers Little Helper;* even though these pills were clearly inscribed with the words, "Valium" on the bottle. There were also vicious Mother and Daughter fights in which conflicting hormones seemed to play a part. It was becoming clear to me that being a Daddy's Girl wasn't such a bad thing after all.

Paula Wagner had become my newest comrade, and I spent hours with the family that bore all the resemblance of our favorite show, *The Brady Bunch.* Her father was a doctor, and her mother a Stay-at-Home Mom who actually baked chocolate chip cookies for us after school. I diligently studied this unfamiliar atmosphere with the eyes of an earnest scholar.

Paula and I had met while volunteering after school to clean the Priest's Rectory at St. Casimir. That particular afternoon, a frigid ice storm was pounding on the classroom windowpane with the tinkling sounds of sharp shards of glass. Sister Bernadette had offered the additional incentive of Brownie Points for those willing to do the housekeeping at the Rectory that day. I secretly wondered about the nun's unconventional approach to cleaning the Priest's quarters herself. Nonetheless, the opportunity to view these mysterious sleeping quarters seemed far more alluring than the alternative of a long walk home in the bitterly cold weather. Our hands shot up simultaneously with Jean Ann, a classmate with dark brunette hair and vivid green eyes, who eagerly came along beside us.

After final instructions from Sister Bernadette, and armed with dusting mops and cloths, we embarked on the dark hallway and into the dank quarters of the Rectory. Other than subtle prayer murmurings that echoed through the corridor from what seemed a series of small bedrooms, the atmosphere seemed tense and forbidden. The Main Living Area was much more cheerful, however, and so we began our tasks with hopes of gaining the promised Brownie Points.

Using my best Elbow Grease, I was just dusting off one of the rich cherry cabinets when the silver knob seemed to slide effortlessly open. "Wow, look at this!" I exclaimed.

Paula and Jean Ann rushed over as we all peered at the contents of the cabinet: Rows of Scotch Whiskey, Rum, and Vodka, lined up like straight little soldiers hiding in captivity. Bottles of red and white wine, and assorted other liquors bearing regal names like *Cognac,* stood guard beside them. Little goblets and glasses twinkled on the shelf above, along with a large crystal decanter filled with a warm amber liquid.

Twisting the large crystal knob, I inhaled the sweet, yet smoky aroma of something that according to Jean Ann was called Sherry. In a moment of Temptation, the promised Brownie Points lost all of their original glamour, as *Alice in Wonderland* seemed to magically take her place among us other three young girls. It was as if she herself were handing us the bottle marked, "Drink Me," that would transport us to another more adventurous time and place.

"Shall We?" we asked each other in unison, as if seeking permission from each other would somehow appease this most mortal of sins.

"Yes!" we shouted in unanimous agreement, sorting through the colorful bottles in anticipation of the perfect antidote that would make our sin worthwhile. Finally, we settled on a bottle of red wine, which after all, was no different in appearance than the strange liquid that we drank every Sunday with the communion wafer.

After a few timid sips, I felt the crimson liquid seep through my belly like warm cough syrup. Courageously, we began to fill our glasses with more of the ruby-red substance. Paula mumbled something that was barely audible, and the sheer secrecy of it all was enough to create a barrage of giggles that could not be suppressed. We howled with laughter and rolled on the floor, the dusting rags pressed to our mouths to muffle the sounds of gaiety that seemed so foreign in these dismal surroundings.

Just when Jean Ann's freckles were taking on a life of their own, a faltering shuffle was heard from the corridor. We quickly slid bottles and glasses back into the cabinet while managing to hide behind the old velvet sofa just seconds before Father Fedewa entered the room. Swinging his right leg with the same solemn gait that had become his trademark, the old priest stopped to steady himself with one arm on the statue of the Virgin Mary. We all pressed our faces into the sofa's musty fabric to avoid the laughter that threatened to escape.

After what seemed hours but in fact was only minutes of extended silence, I peered around the sofa to assess our situation. Father Fedewa had now made his way to the liquor cabinet, as he helped himself to the large crystal decanter of Sherry.

I motioned to Paula and Jean Ann, and we all watched in fascination while the doddering priest stumbled out of the room with the bottle tucked rigidly under his arm, a few drops of the liquid seeping in a trail behind him. The Virgin Mary seemed to watch him as well, her serene blue eyes taking in the incident with a humorous detachment. We all looked up at her with a grateful acknowledgement for choosing not to reveal our little secret.

Nestling the wine bottle firmly back to its rightful dark corner of the cabinet, we scuttled out of the Rectory and into the familiar warmth of the girls bathroom. Pricking our fingers with the pin that Paula had found on the back of her newly dry cleaned uniform, we pressed the slow drops of blood together in grave unity. The three of us were now Official Blood Sisters, and our lives would forever be bound by the dark secret that had confronted us that afternoon.

July 1972

The mosquitoes were humming with a sweet vengeance after the recent rains, while the sun seemed to drop off the water's edge in perfect synchronization with the falling temperature. Paula Wagner and I embraced the welcoming night air with excited anticipation of the evening's events. Our somewhat watered down agenda had been accepted by Paula's parents with surprisingly little effort, and we were not due back for at least four glorious hours.

Both of us were still glowing from the fact that I been given permission to spend the entire month of July as a guest of the Wagner Family lake house. The weeks ahead seemed to stretch out in blissful eternity as we excitedly made the usual plans that would include plenty of sailing, water skiing, marshmallow roasting, and most importantly for the moment, lots of opportunities to meet boys. Summer was the time that Michigan parents everywhere consented to just about anything in their efforts to seek out their own well earned vacation pleasures, and so Mrs. Wagner had merely nodded her approval and waved a coconut encrusted finger as she continued to make fresh Piña Coladas for her sun-worn guests.

In true Michigan tradition, the Summer Families mingled together in their own distinct caste system from The Year Rounders, who were subtly nurturing their seniority. Paula and I ambled beside the lake shore with the confidence of two young teen-age girls who were becoming aware of their sudden effect on men.

"Come ON, you guys!"

The bonfire was just beginning as we slid down the sandy cliffs toward Lake Michigan, weaving our way around the white sand dunes and slender grass reefs with the sure feet of natives who know their terrain. The onyx sky offered a perfect backdrop for the full moon, and the unmistakable fresh scent of burning pine wafted to the tune of the crackling sparks. A bittersweet sensation was gripping my insides as I observed the faces encouraging us to quicken our pace. This was the event that was to mark our graduation from the much-rehearsed Ghost Stories of previous summers. On this evening, we had been chosen as participants in Spin the Bottle, a rite of passage that at that moment threatened to be much spookier than ANY of the familiar stories of my past.

Dave Caruso was shyly peering through the orange flames with an unswerving appreciation of my blossoming new curves. I subconsciously secured the tie of my skimpy, lime-green midriff, wondering if I really should have let Paula sway me into this brash new style. Using the material of my bellbottoms as my sister Jean had taught me, I tried to appear the expert as I opened a cold bottle of beer. The sweet smell of marijuana drifted into the night air and I opted to pass on the small rolled cigarette that was clandestinely handed to me. My brother had just sold me a bag of parsley for fifteen dollars insisting that it was the Real Thing, and I was still nursing my bruised ego from the experience.

My eyes quickly glanced over the fireside circle, half-expecting to see the disapproving expression of Sister Cleophas. Suddenly a wave of relief washed over me as I realized that the world of St. Vincent's could not coexist with the reality of this moment.

The lilting voice of Cat Stevens seemed to seduce us with a quiet lull—adding another forbidden element to the evening's festivities. Paula and I snuggled together under a musty sleeping bag as refuge against the cold night air—reluctant to surrender the familiar comfort of girlhood bonding.

Larry Purdue was announcing the rules of the game in his self-appointed role of Master of Ceremonies. He took on a great air of authority as the green iridescence of the muddied Coke bottle was finding its way around the circle. I silently prayed that the bottle would not go in my direction, since it was well known that Larry would try to take advantage of the situation by sneaking his tongue down your throat.

My heart went out to Paula as the bottle stopped with a determined nod in her direction. She looked at me briefly for assistance, but quickly recognized the unalterable course of her fate as she timidly stepped toward the leering Larry. The two shy teens embraced in a lock that was strictly for the purpose of its viewers, and I only saw a brief struggle on Paula's part as Larry's hand threatened to ride up her plaid kilt skirt. I gave my friend a bright encouraging smile and made room for her once again under the still-warm sleeping bag, feeling her sense of relief that the ordeal was over.

Next, Dave Caruso made his way to the group's center, and with a quick flick of his wrist, sent the bottle spinning in search of its next victim. I watched in silent anticipation as it slowed down to a stop directly in front of me, and with an unexpected confidence, smiled at Dave as we were lured into the circle with the taunting jests of our peers. His pale blue eyes seemed to silently apologize for this intrusion of privacy, before seeking my lips out to be in union with his. Closing my eyes and marveling at the accuracy of lips to make their mark without vision, I slowly melted into the warm primal kiss. While the soft lapping of the Lake Michigan waves evolved into a pounding crescendo, I felt the percussions of a distant beat coursing through my eardrums and weakening my knees.

Reluctantly, I pulled away, pleased that I was now only *slightly* aware of the lingering spirit of Sister Cleophas. It was only after blindly stepped away from the smoky haze of the fire, that I saw the silhouette of the stark black habit as she rose from the flames. Her wrinkled old face twisted into animated contortions of complete disapproval as she shook one crooked finger in admonishment for my behavior. Closing my eyes, I silently extinguished this ghost of my past.

October 2001

The fall winds gusted ferociously over the turbulent waves of Lake Michigan as we trekked up the jagged cliff toward the lake cottage that had been rented for a long weekend in Grand Haven. It was October 5, 2001—exactly thirty-two years to the day since our momentous release from St. Vincent's Home. The horrors of September 11th had brought our family from all corners of the country to gather in our beloved home state.

As we entered the musty old cottage, Lisa assumed her usual mother-hen duties with the refinement of a nurturing innkeeper. As the family scholar, Lisa had gone on to finish her Master's

Degree in social work at Michigan State, and now headed the Crisis Response Team for the Community Mental Health Board of Lansing. She had married Rick Alicia, her childhood sweetheart, and together they had raised two children, Jessica and Ricky Joe.

Lisa's natural leadership abilities had helped to pioneer long-needed changes in the State Mental Health System, and her lobbying efforts were being recognized by local politicians for Mental Health Reform. It seemed a fitting tribute to the same State Capitol building that had once housed our active childhood imaginations. Now, as she opened the dormer windows to the crisp leaves of the aspens and the thundering waves below, we all marveled at the cobalt-blue skies of a Michigan October day that simply did not exist in the various cities that most of us had migrated to over the years.

Theresa, the resourceful travel agent to us all, had once again found the perfect accommodations for our annual family reunion. My little sister had recently survived breast cancer, another reason for our family celebration. Her generous heart and bubbling enthusiasm had not been affected in the slightest by her illness, and we all welcomed back Theresa's radiant spirit as she pitched in to help Lisa in the kitchen with her usual vigor.

Jessica, Lisa's oldest, hauled in tender white birch logs and quickly produced a blazing fire with the determination that seemed to be the driving force behind each new generation of Navarre descendants.

Jean's daughter, Anna, and I giggled as we raced up the stairs to claim the best bedroom. We selected the one with a perfect view of the bright red and white Grand Haven Light House, its circulating beacon of light yet another familiar symbol of a once-carefree world. I picked up a perky little sweater from Anna's suitcase and without her permission, tossed it into The Pile that was already accumulating in the adjoining hallway. Anna, an only child, began to object indignantly. "Hey, I still *like* that sweater!" but then after only minor persuasion, finally gave in as she realized for this week at least, she would have to succumb to our absurd "Peters" traditions.

Joe announced his arrival with a knock on the door downstairs, and we all laughed at his exaggerated expression of fatigue as he pushed my mother's wheelchair in front of the crackling flames of the fire. Her brilliant smile had only become more beautiful over the years, and she beamed proudly at the conversation and laughter of her lively offspring.

Someone turned on the television as a News Bulletin erupted with more government-confirmed information regarding additional Terrorist Attacks, as if to jolt us out of any security we may have been harboring. Our hometown had finally made its way on the map, as Lansing was introduced to America as the silent Hero of the Anthrax vaccination.

We all rolled our eyes, weary of the alarming reports of the disturbing attacks on the New York World Trade Center, wishing to forget for just a few days, the outcome of the unpredictable world that awaited us outside these comforting walls.

"Turn it off!" we all shouted in unison, just as Anna came racing down the stairs with a dusty old book she found in the attic of this charming, thirties-style cottage.

"Look," she announced, "An old book of poems!"

I surveyed her treasure, at once recognizing one of the books that I had read as a child at Gra's House. Lighting candles and retrieving pillows, we all settled in before the fireplace for a good old-fashioned Poetry Reading.

"You know, there's something about this cottage that feels like we've stayed here before," Lisa murmured, lost in thought as she handed me a steamy cup of hot chocolate.

Theresa's daughter, Lindsay, just six months older than Anna, had inherited Theresa's fragile looks and a fiery spirit to match. The young teens playfully took possession of each of my arms as we settled into the soft depths of the old velvet sofa.

The welcoming aura of loving souls seemed to linger in the room with a quiet gentleness, as if in longing to be a part of our festivities. We had lost Cathy McNamara when she was still in her early thirties, to the crippling disease of Alcoholism that had proved to be an unwelcome legacy of her father. A fatal fall down a staircase while Under the Influence had led to the tragic death of our childhood friend.

Our dear father had died of a stroke when I was just twenty years of age and we were all still attending college. It seemed even the perils of Pearl Harbor and the Settlement Of Alaska were no match for the raising of five teen-agers in the seventies. Our beloved Gra had followed suit exactly ten years later. "They're probably still dukin' it out up there," my brother often predicted with a smile.

Joe, now a towering six-foot-four and still bearing a full head of curly black hair along with the mischievous smile of his youth, had become a stable influence and a warm, caring brother who had easily stepped in to become The Family Patriarch after my father had died. A "Lifer" with the phone company, he was looking forward to early retirement at only forty-five years of age. It was just like my brother to find a way to Beat The System.

My mother, the picture of contentment as she studied each of us with tender affection, was oblivious to the recent news events. Though the new pharmaceuticals for Schizophrenia had shown an amazing improvement in her mental abilities, the long years of institutions had left their weary mark upon her. Ironically, the cocoon of illusion that often characterized this strange disease now seemed to insulate her from the current world violence like an unexpected gift.

The information concerning my mother's budding mental illness that I had been searching for as a child was revealed to me much later in life by my Uncle George. Apparently, it was during the early part of her marriage that a mysterious aura began to cast a shadow over my mother's delicate features.

"She would sometimes have to be called back to the conversation at hand," he recalled. "However, your mother was so charming that these lapses were easily dismissed as her famous smile came flooding back with an unspoken apology for the short interruption."

I could picture my mother fighting for her sanity, like a flickering candle gasping for oxygen in order to sustain its flame—and the friends who must have attributed these brief respites to the absent-minded nature of a skilled artist who might be mentally unveiling yet another masterpiece, if only on the canvas of the imagination.

Uncle George had shielded his hand over his eyes to look at me more closely through the outdoor sunlight of a Las Vegas casino that day. "You have her eyes," he added.

And Leatrice? Many years after our St. Vincent's days, as I patiently waited in the passenger seat for my Michigan State date to return with his Marlboro cigarettes, I encountered Leatrice at the Mobil Station on campus. I was busy amusing myself by exhaling warm circles on the frigid window of the 1956 red Corvette and contemplating how I was going to ease out of my uninteresting date.

Suddenly, I spotted the frantic waving through the window of another vehicle that was parked at the pump beside us. Without any invitation whatsoever, a tall, willowy, beautiful black girl opened the door. I watched as one perfect Italian shoe slid in next to me on the drivers' side. If it weren't for the familiar grin, I would never have recognized our long-lost Soul Sister.

We screamed and hugged in utter delight, as I took in the elegant clothes and beautiful thick black hair that fell down her back in a cascade of curls. Leatrice informed me that she was living in Detroit, and, not to my surprise, had a successful modeling career.

All too soon, my faceless date was back with his cigarettes, and Leatrice seemed to evaporate from the car as suddenly as she had entered. A tall, handsome black man was watching us with curiosity as he quietly opened her door and Leatrice gracefully stepped into a shiny new red Mercedes.

As I tried to grasp what seemed so familiar about Leatrice, it suddenly dawned on me: Leatrice had all the poise, body language, and even the slight Midwestern twang of my sisters and me. In turn, we had inherited the carefree ways and natural rhythm of her dominant culture. Yes, the exchange had certainly been a fair one, and I was grateful for the gifts that we had left each other in our formative years.

You're a jewel, Jeannie," my mother was saying in grateful response to the new slippers that were being snuggled over her frail old feet. Having taken the usual head count of her five children, she was content now to watch us interact playfully from the comfort of her wheelchair.

Years before her illness—perhaps anticipating the troubling future we would encounter—my mother had prayed that her children would be granted the gift of an enduring friendship together. It was evident through the warm and easy camaraderie we shared, that an unbreakable thread had woven its way through each of our lives, and that this particular prayer had indeed been heard.

Jean was celebrating her new ownership of a Bed and Breakfast Inn, which she had successfully combined with a large interior design showroom. The once-firm resolve to maintain her independence was now an asset as she wholeheartedly tackled new endeavors with a fiery entrepreneurial spirit. I watched now as my sister responded to my mother's' contentment by returning the gentle gaze with a twinkle of remarkably similar aqua green eyes.

In that moment, it occurred to me that there was something else exuding from my mother with the brilliance of my beloved Star of Christina—a quality that had become as refined as the Monet paintings that she had once so vividly captured on canvas. Something that can only be earned through OUR weakness and GOD'S strength. My mother had perfected the mastery of love. It was obvious that neither this tormenting disease, nor the government systems that struggled to control it, could ever replace the powerful instincts of a mother's devotion.

In the kitchen, someone discovered a towel that bore the faded design of a red, white and blue flag - a symbol of America's exaggerated patriotism that was suddenly springing up from a dormant past. As if to apologize to our nation for temporarily ignoring its current plight, Theresa posted it above the roaring fireplace. As the stars and stripes flickered in the light of the burning embers, it seemed a humble, yet appropriate offering to our country.

I was suddenly propelled to the front porch, lured by the lighthouse beam that was casting its rotating beacon over the frothy tops of the lapping waves with a consistent, soothing rhythm. Shivering, I wrapped my brother's green and white Michigan State sweatshirt around my shoulders to ward off the sharp autumn chill. A colorful array of burnt orange and yellow maple leaves twirled at my feet in a rapid crescendo. The years of clinging to the solid old tree seemed to have finally weakened the blackened veins of the leaves, and they shed their ties from the familiar branches with a crackling swirl of relief.

Settling into an old wicker chair, I thought about my life so far. Like a kaleidoscope of shapes and patterns that seemed to never evolve into one piece, my life had proven to be a series of constant challenges and blessings.

After a decade of attempting to reform The Corporate World, I had finally given up, and had succeeded in building my own Interior Design firm. The crude Hawaiian girl painting that had hovered over my bedroom walls for years must have been sending her own subliminal message. Even so, it seemed ironic that I had now found a way to get paid instead of punished for my creative visions. The gift of Freedom, denied me as a child, had guided me along life's paths as surely as this ever-searching lighthouse beam, bringing travel and new experiences in place of the more conforming traditions of marriage and children. True, the years of being motherless had not been without their emotional perils.

But now, even that deep-rooted value was currently being threatened with the addition of a solid new love in my life. And speaking of roots that don't respond easily to the Round Up of Life's Lessons, my Catholic values were as strong today as the day they were planted. Curiously enough, these values which promise to Protect Human Life, To Promote Human Dignity, To Defend The Poor, And To Seek The Common Good in all people, had been a Tough Cross to Bear for those that still scoffed at the gemstone-rose-colored glasses of my youth. It was with a slow but steady awareness, that I had discovered the Realities of Life's Lessons, were sadly not always in alignment with those learned truths.

Sighing, I stood to join the others just as one of the smallest leaves, brilliant in repose, hesitated only slightly before snuggling into one of the many growing piles that fringed the old redwood planks—as if happily secure in her comfortable new environment.

Anna had the spotlight as she stood poised in front of the fire for the next poetry reading.

"Get *on* with it!" my brother was saying as he threw a pillow at her with his usual compassion. After only a brief interruption to return the pillow with admirable force to her Uncle Joe's head, Anna continued in a soft-spoken voice, gaining confidence as she read:

A little bird I am,
Shut from the fields of air,
And in my cage I sit and sing
To Him who placed me there;
But though my wings are closely bound,
My soul is as liberty;
For prison walls cannot control
The flight or freedom of the soul.
L.B. Cowman

After a breakfast of Walnut Pancakes, sausage and fresh Michigan maple syrup, we set out for the day's excursion, pleasantly surprised that we had not lost our usual talent for cramming into a vehicle. The Final Vote was to view the brilliant Fall foliage of the Lelenau Peninsula via Joe's SUV, with all the appropriate stops at the Wineries, the Traverse City Boutiques, and finally, the Gra-inspired Old Bowers Inn for dinner.

The fallen white birch logs and sparkling green waters of the creamy shoreline seemed to counter the recent news events with a sweet innocence, while plump billowy clouds hovered above, their haunting, iridescent beauty radiating the unspoken message that we were never *really* in charge, after all.

As the crimson and ginger foliage of the turning leaves blurred past my window, we all seemed lost in our own personal thoughts. From my usual left-hand corner in the back seat, I observed my mother's calm, peaceful expression with a new gratitude for the slow but steady progress that the medical world had achieved toward treating this puzzling disease. Just then the long smoldering ember of her cigarette unfurled into a luminous thread of silvery ash before dropping unceremoniously to the floor of the car. My greatest fear, I acknowledged to myself, had just been realized, and yet not one of us had ever gone up into the proverbial smoke I had imagined.

Lisa allowed the car to sway haphazardly for just a moment, and then winked at me playfully as we all began to laugh. Somewhere from the front seat, a distant melody began to drift, the words now piercing the air with a whole different meaning from that of my youth. As Americans, we would always own the delicious freedom to choose our beliefs—a liberty that would forever prevail over our radically humbled nation and that of its proud, resilient families.

"I looked out the window and what did I see . . ."

Three generations of Navarres and at least one Gentle Spirit responded with a resounding chorus:

"POPCORN POPPIN' ON THE APRICOT TREE!"

HICKORY NUT CAKE

2 eggs
1 C. brown sugar
1 C. thick sour cream
1/4 tsp. soda
pinch of salt
1 3/4 C. flour
1 1/2 tsp. baking powder
1 C ground hickory nuts
1 tsp. vanilla

Beat the eggs; add the brown sugar and mix well. Mix together the sour cream, soda and salt. Add to sugar and egg mixture. Add the flour, baking powder, nuts and vanilla. Mix well, pour into greased and floured pans and bake at 350 degrees for 45 minutes to one hour.

SLIDERS-GLISSADES

2 cups flour
1/2 C. chicken fat or lard
pinch of salt
1/2 tsp. baking powder
Add enough water to form pie-like dough

Roll dough about 1/2 inch thick and cut in 2 inch squares. Cook over stewed chicken or chicken broth for 20 minutes in covered pan. Do not uncover until done.

OLD FASHIONED STRAWBERRY SHORTCAKE

2 1/4 C. sifted Flour
4 t. baking powder
2 T. Sugar
1/4 t. salt
6 T. butter or margarine
1 egg, beaten
1 C. milk
1 quart strawberries

1. Sift flour, baking powder, sugar, salt, and butter into mixture with knives until coarse
2. Blend egg and milk and pour into dry ingredients: mix with fork until all flour is moistened. (A light touch here–don't handle dough too much)
3. Divide into two parts and spread out in two, greased, 8" tins.
4. Bake in oven at 450 degrees about 20 minutes or until golden brown.
5. Add fresh strawberries lightly sweetened with cane sugar and spread between and over each biscuit.
6. Top with fresh whipped cream lightly sweetened with vanilla

BRAZIL NUT CAKE

1 C. boiling water
1 C. chopped pitted dates (approx. 1/2 pound)
1 tsp. baking soda
3 T. shortening
1 C. granulated sugar
1 egg, beaten
1 C. coarsely chopped Brazil Nuts
2 C. sifted cake four
1/2 tsp. salt
1 tsp. vanilla

Pour water over dates, add soda and let stand until cool; work shortening with sugar until smooth; beat in egg. Sift flour with salt and alternate with date mixture. Stir in nuts and vanilla.

FROSTING (Double recipe for 2-layer cake)

1/4 C. brown sugar,
3/4 C. granulated sugar
1/2 C. light cream
1/2 C. milk
1 T. butter

Bring to boil (do not stir) Cook until soft ball stage. Take from stove and beat until creamy.

MOTHER'S OLD FASHIONED WHITE SUGAR COOKIES

(Rosie Trabbic Drouillard)

2 C. sugar
1 C. butter
1 C. sour cream
1 tsp. baking soda
1 tsp. salt
2 eggs
1/4 teaspoon nutmeg
flour as needed

Combine sugar and butter and cream well. Add the 2 eggs beaten to these ingredients and again stir and cream well. Then add the sour cream with 1 tsp soda, stir up and pour into previous ingredients and still well again. Add nutmeg and flour

Bake in a 375 oven until done.

BAKED APPLE BUTTER

12 pounds of apples: Jonathan, Winesap or Northern Spy

Cut them into quarters. Nearly cover with water. Cook gently for about 1 and 1/2 hours. Put the pulp through a fine strainer. Measure it. Allow to each cup of pulp:

1/2 cup sugar
Add:
3 tsp. cinnamon
1 1/2 tsp. cloves
1/2 tsp. allspice

Bring these ingredients to the boiling point. Cool and add:
1 cup dry white wine

Place about 3/4 of the puree in a large heatproof crock. Keep the rest in reserve. Put the crock in a cold over. Set oven at 300 degrees. Permit the apple butter to bake until it thickens. As it shrinks, fill the crock with reserved apple butter. When the butter is thick, but still moist, put into sterile jars for keeping.

ELEANORS CREAMED CRABMEAT IN PATTY SHELLS

(As served at White House luncheon)

2 T. butter
2 T. flour
1 C. milk
1 tsp. salt
1/2 tsp. pepper
2 cups crab meat–cut into small pieces
(Optional–1 tsp. curry powder)

Make a white sauce with butter, flour and milk, add seasonings and crab meat and serve in patty shells

PECAN ROLLS

1 C. lukewarm water
3 T. shortening
1 tsp. salt
1/4C. sugar

Mix the above and add 1 yeast cake dissolved in 1/4 cup water and 1 beaten egg.

Add:

3 1/2 cups flour, sifted, put in refrigerator over night or at least for a few hours (covered with a towel)

Take out, shape into large ball, cover and let rise until double in bulk, then roll dough on a floured board to the thickness of 1/4 inch. Spread generously with melted butter. Sprinkle generously with cinnamon and brown sugar. Roll the dough like a jelly roll. Cut into 1 and a half inch slices. Put 2 teaspoons melted butter and 2 teaspoons brown sugar in bottom of each muffin tin with a few pecans and place slices on top.

Bake in 350 degree oven till brown (about 20 minutes) Watch closely–you may want to turn heat down so brown sugar bottom doesn't burn.

STRAWBERRY-RHUBARB JAM

3 cups strawberries
3 cups diced rhubarb
5 cups sugar

Bring to rolling boil and then boil for about 8 minutes.

FRENCH DOUGHNUTS

3 C. all purpose flour
1 package of active dry yeast
1/2 tsp. ground nutmeg
1 C. milk
1/4 C. sugar
1/4 C. cooking oil
3/4 tsp. salt
1 egg
Confectioner's sugar

In large bowl combine 1 3/4 cup of the flour with the yeast and nutmeg. In saucepan, heat milk, sugar, oil and salt just until warm, stirring occasionally. Add yeast mixture: add egg. Beat at low speed in electric mixed for 1/2 minute, scraping sides of bowl constantly. Beat 3 min. at low speed. By hand, stir enough of remaining flour to make soft dough. Turn into greased bowl, cover and chill. Form dough into ball, cover and let rest 10 minutes. Roll dough to 18 x 12 inch rectangle. Cut in 3x2 inch rectangles, cover, let rise 30 minutes. Fry a few at a time in deep fat (375 degrees), turning once until golden brown, (about 1 minute). Drain on paper toweling; sprinkle with confectioner's sugar. Makes 36 doughnuts. Serve warm.

TATE PUBLISHING *& Enterprises*

Tate Publishing is committed to excellence in the publishing industry. Our staff of highly trained professionals, including editors, graphic designers, and marketing personnel, work together to produce the very finest books available. The company reflects the philosophy established by the founders, based on Psalms 68:11,

"THE LORD GAVE THE WORD AND GREAT WAS THE COMPANY OF THOSE WHO PUBLISHED IT."

If you would like further information, please call
1.888.361.9473
or visit our website
www.tatepublishing.com

TATE PUBLISHING *& Enterprises*, LLC
127 E. Trade Center Terrace
Mustang, Oklahoma 73064 USA